BIBLE
Crosswords
Collection #9

Compiled and Edited
by *Ellyn Sanna*

BARBOUR
PUBLISHING, INC.
Uhrichsville, Ohio

Published by Barbour Publishing, Inc.
　　　　　P.O. Box 719
　　　　　Uhrichsville, Ohio 44683
　　　　　http://www.barbourbooks.com

 Member of the
Evangelical Christian
Publishers Association

Printed in the United States of America.

BIBLE
Crosswords
Collection #9

ACROSS

1. "Abraham built an _____"
   (Gen. 22:9)
5. "After these _____" (Gen. 22:1)
10. Public transportation
12. Needed for a shower
13. "Where is the lamb for a _____
    offering?" (Gen. 22:7)
14. Irish freedom fighters, abbr.
16. Peter said, "_____ , we have left
    all" (Mark 10:28)
17. Male pronoun
18. "_____ took all the silver"
    (1 Kings 15:18)
19. Study for an exam
21. Exclamation
22. Asian beast of burden
24. Concern
26. Isaac's replacement
    (Gen. 22:13)
28. First person pronoun
29. Place where Mary and Joseph
    found no room
30. Preposition that indicates
    belonging
32. Where Abraham went to
    sacrifice Isaac (Gen. 22:2)
34. He "laid the wood _____ order"
    (Gen. 22:9)
37. "God will _____" (Gen. 22:8)
39. "I and the lad will _____ yonder"
    (Gen. 22:5)
40. Company, abbr.
41. The opposite of followed
42. Irish county, abbr.
43. Lemon thirst quencher
44. Elongated fish
46. "Abraham and the _____ went
    together" (Gen. 22:5)
48. Adjective suffix indicating
    nationality or "somewhat"

49. Simile preposition
50. "Abraham rose up _____"
    (Gen. 22:3)
51. Abraham took three _____ to
    reach the mountain (Gen. 22:4)

DOWN

2. The kind of job your car needs
3. "God tested _____"
   (Gen. 22:1 NIV)
4. What a baseball player wants
5. Where the ram was caught
   (Gen. 22:13)
6. Abraham's son
7. Negative
8. Guy's date
9. Voiced
11. "None can _____ his hand"
    (Dan. 4:35)
15. Transportation on tracks, abbr.
17. The story's main character
20. Northeastern state
21. Either
23. Sky fellow, abbr.
25. Nurses, abbr.
27. Where Abraham was told to go
    (Gen. 22:2)
31. _____ up, excited
33. "The _____ of the Lord called
    unto him" (Gen. 22:11)
35. A swollen mass of tissue
36. The _____ was laid on the altar
    (Gen. 22:9)
37. "Abraham. . .saw the _____ afar
    off" (Gen. 22:4)
38. "Abraham lifted up his _____"
    (Gen. 22:4)
40. School group
42. "Pharaoh. . .sought to _____
    Moses" (Exod. 2:15)
45. Inquiring noise

47. Overhead train

by Elizabeth B. Smith

ACROSS

1. Moses's brother
5. People who make cloth by interlacing threads
11. Possible undergraduate degree for a minister, abbr.
12. Not yes
13. Do not ____ to the words of the prophecy (Rev. 22:18)
14. Black sticky substance
15. Infant
17. ____ of the Chaldees
18. Preposition that indicates location
20. Burnt offering for peace to the Lord (Exod. 24:5)
22. Aromatic substances (Exod. 25:6)
25. Sympathetic noise
26. Hole
27. Name for Mother
28. "____ a child is known by his doings" (Prov. 20:11)
30. Control
32. Something given to God
34. The color of the Tabernacle's ram skins (Exod. 25:5)
35. The language of Cervantes, abbr.
36. Head
38. The beings whose wings cover the mercy seat (Exod. 25:20)
43. Address abbreviation
45. Opposite of off
46. Selenium, chem. symbol
47. Eleven, Rom. num.
48. Ancient
49. Metal taken as a Tabernacle offering (Exod. 25:3)
51. Why Jesus died
52. Place near Bethel (Gen. 13:3 NIV)
53. Young adult, abbr.
54. Greatest Christian virtue
55. Fabric dyed blue, purple, and scarlet for the Tabernacle (Exod. 25:4)
56. Silver, chem. symbol
57. The priest who took care of Hannah's son Samuel

DOWN

1. Short for Abigail
2. Woman's name
3. Stone worn on Aaron's shoulders (Exod. 28:9, 12)
4. A denial
5. Armed conflict
6. Edward, for short
7. Adjust
8. Alien from space, abbr.
9. "Let us run with patience the ____ that is set before us" (Heb. 12:1)
10. Jr.'s father
16. Kind of tie
17. Not, prefix
19. Note on the scale
21. "The Lord shall reign for ____" (Exod. 15:18)
22. "Trees of the wood ____ out" (1 Chron. 16:33)
23. "Enter. . .into his ____ with praise" (Ps. 100:4)
24. "Thy ____ will I establish" (Ps. 89:4)
25. American Academy of Family Physicians, abbr.
26. Writing instrument
27. The man God sent to deliver the Israelites from the Egyptians
29. Contender
31. Shelter from the wind

33. Jewish priest's outer vestment
36. Greek letter
37. Friend, Fr.
39. Printer's measure, approximately half of an em
40. United Service Organizations, abbr.
41. Beautiful, Ital.
42. Mountain where Moses talked with God
44. "They ____ not, neither do they spin" (Matt. 6:28)
47. Greek letter
49. Past tense of gin

50. "A ____ returneth to his vomit" (Prov. 26:11)
51. "That we may ____ and believe" (Mark 15:32)
53. Old-fashioned you

PUZZLE 3

ACROSS

1. Biblical river
6. Longest book in the Bible
11. Female friends, Fr.
12. "There is death in the ____"
    (2 Kings 4:40)
13. Where those who are alive will
    meet the Lord when He comes
    again (1 Thess. 4:17)
14. "He esteemeth ____ as straw"
    (Job 41:27)
15. "She. . .hid them with the ____
    of flax" (Josh. 2:6)
16. Ceremonial form of prayer
19. Asian tree
20. When you'll get there, more or
    less, abbr.
22. John the Baptist's was made of
    camel hair (Matt. 3:4)
25. What a baby needs changed
28. Hesitant syllable
29. Jonathan shot this to warn David
    not to return to Saul's house
32. Route, abbr.
33. Joseph's brothers had these
    searched to find his silver cup
36. The eleventh letter of the
    Hebrew alphabet
37. Exclamation of surprise and
    triumph
38. God sent Jonah to warn this city
40. The wise men
41. Put off till a later time
42. Exist
43. Article that precedes a vowel
44. Firstborn son of Isaac and
    Rebecca
45. Chum
46. Severely
49. Bitter water was turned to this
    at Marah
50. Abraham's father

DOWN

1. Man charged to keep Paul and
   Silas safe in prison (Acts 16:23)
2. Sixth king of Israel
   (1 Kings 16:16)
3. Violent public disturbance
4. Small silver coin of ancient
   Rome
5. Preposition used in a simile
6. "We are the clay, and thou our
   ____" (Isa. 64:8)
7. "The Lord. . .purposed it to ____
   the pride" (Isa. 23:9)
8. "Cast alive into a ____ of fire"
   (Rev. 19:20)
9. How God first watered the earth
10. Twelfth-grader, abbr.
12. Addendum at the end of the
    letter, abbr.
17. Told by Elisha to wash himself
    seven times in the River Jordan
18. Yelp
21. Albert's nickname
23. One of the Spirit's fruit, a
    lowly spirit
24. Modern-day country where
    Noah's Ark is rumored to be
26. Spinning toy
27. Son of Kishi (1 Chron. 6:44)
30. Cheer
31. Ezekiel saw this in his visions
32. Sixth book of the New Testament
34. Apple drink
35. Psalm word
39. Burial chamber
42. "Valley of ____" (Ps. 84:6)
46. Masculine pronoun
47. Preposition indicating location
48. King James Version of you

PUZZLE 4

ACROSS

1. Father of the Chosen People (Gen. 12:1–3)
8. Prophet who tore his cloak into twelve pieces (1 Kings 11:30)
13. Sheep's noise
14. Old Testament prophet, between Amos and Jonah
17. Brief letter
18. Samuel's mentor
19. The rock city of Idumaea (Isa. 16:1)
20. No-good fellow
22. Lions failed to harm him
23. Third longest book of prophecy in the Old Testament
24. Northern central state, abbr.
25. Drill instructor, abbr.
26. King of Israel (1 Kings 16:16)
27. Jacob's son (Gen. 30:10–11)
28. Belonging to a son of Aaron (1 Chron. 24:1)
32. This animal alive is better than a dead lion (Eccles. 9:4)
33. Belonging to the man who shot Jehoram through the heart (2 Kings 9:24)
35. Nehemiah's priest and scribe
39. Eliasaph was the son of this man (Num. 7:42)
41. A servant in the house of Saul (2 Sam. 9:2)
44. "All they that hate me love ____" (Prov. 8:36)
46. Asian woman's garment
47. Abraham's son
48. "Cursed is the ____ who. . . sacrifices a blemished animal to the Lord" (Mal. 1:14 NIV)
50. This place in Moab was ruined in the night (Isa. 15:1)
51. "____! The gate to the nations is broken" (Ezek. 26:2 NIV)
52. The judge and prophet who established the kingship in Israel (1 Sam. 8:21–22)
53. His wife became a pillar of salt
54. The Lord showed him a plumbline

56. Chemical symbol for argon
57. "Prophet of the Temple" and a colleague of Zechariah (Ezra 5:1)
59. "The name of the wicked shall ____" (Prov. 10:7)
61. Needed for a photograph
64. Unit of dry measurement, abbr.
65. Moses successor (Num. 27:18–23)
68. One of the twelve spies, the only one left alive in the desert with Joshua (Num. 26:65)
70. Exist
72. Cast a ballot
73. Sleuth, abbr.
74. "I will spread my ____ upon them" (Hos. 7:12)
75. David's father

DOWN

1. In bed
2. The mercenary prophet (Num. 22:5–7)
3. "I will ____ bread from heaven" (Exod. 16:4)
4. Prophet who married Gomer
5. Killed by his brother
6. Last book of the Old Testament, abbr.
7. Joshua sent men there from Jericho (Josh. 7:2)
8. King of Judah at 22 years old who reigned for only a year (2 Kings 8:26)
9. Opposite of out
10. He was 8 years old when he became king and he reigned for 31 years (2 Kings 22:1)
11. Preposition
12. State of everlasting separation from God
15. Israel's poet king
16. Did perfectly on a test
21. Eastern seaboard state
24. "The ____ of sin is death" (Rom. 6:23)
26. Son of Boaz (Ruth 4:21)
27. Appeared to Abraham when he was 99 years old (Gen. 17:1)

29. Ezekiel's father (Ezek. 1:3)
30. Egyptian goddess
31. Juan's yes
33. The weeping prophet
34. Word said by Christ on the cross (Matt. 27:46)
36. Second from the last book of the Old Testament
37. The son of Shema and the father of Jorkoam (1 Chron. 2:43)
38. Consumed
40. United Airlines, abbr.
42. Ahab served this god (1 Kings 16:31)
43. Supported Moses' hands in battle (Exod. 17:8–13)
45. "A ____ word stirs up anger" (Prov. 15:1 NIV)
49. King Darius threw Daniel here (Dan. 6:16)

52. The youngest son of Hiel of Bethel, who lost his life when the gates of Jericho were set up (1 Kings 16:34)
55. The man to whom God gave the Ten Commandments
56. American Football Conference, abbr.
58. Fifth month of the Jewish year
59. Decays
60. Chemical symbol for thorium
62. Lending library, abbr.
63. "I will make you fishers of ____" (Matt. 4:19)
65. Joseph for short
66. The opposite of down
67. To trouble, afflict
69. Chemical symbol for beryllium
71. Estimated position, abbr.
72. Video jockey, abbr.

by Michael J. Landi

PUZZLE 5

ACROSS

1. "Give me this ____" (John 4:15)
5. "____ of false prophets" (Matt. 7:15)
10. Jacque's friend
11. Noncommissioned officer, abbr.
12. Angry
14. "Behold the ____ of God" (John 1:29)
16. Small child
17. "Set your affection on things above, not on things on the ____" (Col. 3:2)
20. "Cleanse your ____" (James 4:8)
24. Dessert
25. "Ye have not because ye ____ not" (James 4:2)
26. "Set thy ____ among the stars" (Obad. 1:4)
27. New England state, abbr.
28. Abram's nephew
30. The son of Peleth (Num. 16:1)
31. "God gave the ____" (1 Cor. 3:6)
34. Ruth's second husband (Ruth 4:13)
35. Masculine pronoun
36. "At thy word I will let down the ____" (Luke 5:5)
37. "Every ____ shall see him" (Rev. 1:7)
39. Summer beverage
40. Alternating current, abbr.
41. "The ____ of those things is death" (Rom. 6:21)
44. Spoken
46. "____ thy foot against a stone" (Matt. 4:6)
48. God gave Joshua the victory over ____ (Josh. 8:1)
50. "Clothed in pure and white ____" (Rev. 15:6)
51. Nicodemus was a ____ of the Jews (John 3:1)
53. Alcoholic beverage
54. The Creator
55. "There is none good but ____" (Mark 10:18)

DOWN

1. "We ____ by faith" (2 Cor. 5:7)
2. Japanese pearl diver
3. "Grace to help in ____ of need" (Heb. 4:16)
4. Nurse, abbr.
5. "____ young men, and maidens" (Ps. 148:12)
6. "None is able to ____ thee" (2 Chron. 20:6)
7. Relating or resembling, suffix
8. "Who giveth ____ upon the earth" (Job 5:10)
9. And, Lat.
13. Elevated trains
15. To immerse or dip in water
18. Smallest state, abbr.
19. "A ____ of babes" (Rom. 2:20)
21. Largest state, abbr.
22. Dead letter office, abbr.
23. Genus, comb. form
25. Score an A
26. "These were more ____ than those in Thessalonica" (Acts 17:11)
28. "If thou ____ this man go" (John 19:12)
29. "False ____ among you" (2 Pet. 2:1)
32. Regarding, abbr.
33. The ____ is the word of God (Luke 8:11)
38. "Teach the ____ women" (Titus 2:4)

39. Louisiana's neighbor, abbr.
40. Preposition
42. "She put her hand to the ____" (Judg. 5:26)
43. "Jesus saith unto them, Come and ____." (John 21:12)
45. "Paul the ____" (Philem. 9)
47. "____ to keep you from falling" (Jude 24)
49. Male sibling, for short
50. City in California, abbr.
52. International peace-keeping organization, abbr.

by Carole Stengel

PUZZLE 6

ACROSS

1. "Receive his mark in his ____, or in his hand" (Rev. 14:9)
7. "If the foot shall say, Because I am not the ____, I am not of the body" (1 Cor. 12:15)
10. Imperial Chemical Industries, abbr.
11. "In the day thou wast born thy ____ was not cut" (Ezek. 16:4)
12. Bird's beak
13. "Let ____ esteem other better than themselves" (Phil. 2:3)
14. Speed measurement, abbr.
15. Car fuel
16. Peruvian beast of burden
18. The letter that follows "em"
20. East Indies, abbr.
21. Either
22. "Fall by the ____ of the sword" (Luke 21:24)
24. Activity or movement
26. Preposition
27. Fifteen, Rom. num.
28. Wing of a building
29. "I am escaped with the skin of my ____" (Job 19:20)
32. The letter that precedes "em"
34. "A man's pride shall bring him ____" (Prov. 29:23)
36. "The government shall be upon his ____" (Isa. 9:6)
40. Midwest state, abbr.
41. Negative
43. Last, prefix
44. Violent group
45. Sticky
46. "God. . .spake in time ____ unto the fathers by the prophets" (Heb. 1:1)
49. First person plural pronoun

50. Female, suffix
51. Sheep's noise
52. And so on, Lat. abbr.
53. Verb of being
54. "The ____ of every man is Christ" (1 Cor. 11:3)

DOWN

1. "Jesus. . .with his ____ wrote on the ground" (John 8:6)
2. The Atlantic or Pacific
3. "The Lord God. . .took one of his ____ , and closed up the flesh" (Gen. 2:21)
4. "Thou shalt bruise his ____" (Gen. 3:15)
5. "Immediately his feet and ____ bones received strength" (Acts 3:7 O.E. spelling)
6. Flower
7. Fifth letter of the Hebrew alphabet
8. Soul, Lat.
9. Remove horns
17. The widow's ____
19. Edward, for short
21. Kind of tea
22. "Having ____, see ye not?" (Mark 8:18)
23. Used-to-be, prefix
25. "Love worketh no ____ to his neighbour" (Rom 13:10)
26. Exist
29. "The ____ is a little member" (James 3:5)
30. "Take of his blood. . .upon the ____ of their right hand" (Exod. 29:20)
31. "____, is the Lord of Hosts" (Isa. 6:3)
32. Word reviser, abbr.

33. "They brake not his ____" (John 19:33)
35. First person plural pronoun
37. Arizona's neighbor, abbr.
38. "Only her ____ moved, but her voice was not heard" (1 Sam. 1:13)
39. Rodent
42. To drive out
47. The remains of burned wood
48. "With the ____ bone of an ass . . . have I slain a thousand men" (Judg. 15:16)
50. Printer's measure

51. Minister's undergraduate degree, abbr.

PUZZLE 7

ACROSS

1. Cut
7. "He fell into a ____" (Acts 10:10)
13. Declares
14. "The son of Geber, in ____-gilead" (1 Kings 4:13)
15. Jesus' birthplace
17. Exist
19. The number of commandments God gave Moses
20. "____, every one that thirsteth" (Isa. 55:1)
22. Animal that Christ rode on Palm Sunday
24. Depend on others' money
26. "Whether it be good or ____" (2 Cor. 5:10)
27. Activity
29. "Then an ____ cried aloud" (Dan. 3:4)
31. Pertaining to air, prefix
32. "God hath given ____ unto your brethren" (Josh. 22:4)
33. Hastens
35. "The seed is ____ under their clods" (Joel 1:17)
37. Vigor
38. "____ died without children" (1 Chron. 2:30)
40. When you think you'll get there, abbr.
41. Three feet, abbr.
43. Relative, abbr.
45. Part of the blood that carries iron, abbr.
46. "The Lord fulfil all thy ____" (Ps. 20:5)
50. "This Agar is Mount Sinai in ____" (Gal. 4:25)
52. "We have had ____ to eat" (2 Chron. 31:10)
55. "The ____ is not dead, but sleepeth" (Mark 5:39)
56. "Thou shalt utterly ____ it" (Deut. 7:26)

DOWN

1. Verb of being
2. The Bible's new covenant, abbr.
3. Taxi
4. Article
5. Place
6. Mehir was the father of ____ (1 Chron. 4:11)
7. "He made a ____ about the altar" (1 Kings 18:32)
8. Cheer
9. "Surely I come quickly. ____" (Rev. 22:20)
10. Name, Fr.
11. Massachusetts' neighbor
12. Questioning noise
16. Man's name
17. Sheep noise
18. "There ____ not a man of them" (1 Sam. 30:17)
20. "I will save her that ____" (Zeph. 3:19)
21. "The ____ number of them is to be redeemed" (Num. 3:48)
23. Sharply inclined
24. Emotions
25. "They should not return to ____" (Matt. 2:12)
26. Sew quickly
28. Anger
30. Return, abbr.
33. "Who came in privily to ____ out our liberty" (Gal. 2:4)
34. Appearing in consecutive parts

35. "They _____ upon the Lord God of their fathers" (2 Chron. 13:18)
36. Seize for arrest
39. "I will _____ you go"(Exod. 8:28)
42. "Their _____ shall not become garments" (Isa. 59:6)
44. Nautical mile
46. Girl's nickname
47. "_____ them about thy neck" (Prov. 6:21)
48. "The Lord our God is_____ Lord" (Mark 12:29)
49. "If any man will _____ thee at the law" (Matt. 5:40)
50. Commercial, abbr.

51. Radium, chem. symbol
53. Organization for young females, abbr.
54. Altitude, abbr.

by Evelyn M. Boyington

ACROSS

1. "I am the ____ ____ ____, and the lily of the valleys" (Song of Sol. 2:1) (3 words)
9. Not out
10. Timid
11. On or about, abbr.
12. "I am the ____ ____, and know my sheep" (John 10:14) (2 words)
17. Immerse briefly in water
18. Central state, Des Moines is the capital, abbr.
20. "I am the way, ____ ____, and the life" (John 14:6) (2 words)
24. "Behold the ____ of God" (John 1:29)
26. Extraterrestial, abbr.
27. Suffix
28. "____, every one that thirsteth" (Isa. 55:1)
29. Two, Rom. num.
31. "The ____ ____ ____ is Lord even of the sabbath" (Matt. 12:8) (3 words)
34. "We have not ____ this power" (1 Cor. 9:12)
37. Network, especially of blood vessels
38. Learning disabled, abbr.
39. "Jesus Christ, the ____ ____ ____" (Mark 1:1) (3 words)
42. Certified Public Accountant, abbr.
43. Containing oxygen, prefix
44. Dorothy's state, abbr.
45. Head nurse, abbr.
46. "Lest I ____ you in pieces" (Ps. 50:22)
48. "The Spirit of God descending like a ____" (Matt. 3:16)
51. Took a chair

53. "I am the ____" (John 14:6)
54. "I am. . .the bright and ____ ____" (Rev. 22:16) (2 words)

DOWN

1. "An advocate with the Father, Jesus Christ the ____" (1 John 2:1)
2. "Who built ____, and Lod" (1 Chron. 8:12)
3. Compose, var. form
4. Follicle stimulating hormone, abbr.
5. Feminine pronoun
6. Hypothesis, abbr.
7. "Let her be as the loving hind and pleasant ____" (Prov. 5:19)
8. Paddle
13. Poem
14. Nimble
15. Masculine pronoun
16. "His eyes were ____, so that he could not see" (Gen. 27:1)
19. "According to his ____ mercy" (1 Pet. 1:3)
21. Altitude, abbr.
22. Thorough, nonstandard spelling
23. Sharpened
24. "I am the bread of ____" (John 6:35)
25. Direct toward a target
30. Understanding
32. Writings that contain the old covenant, abbr.
33. "I am ____ and Omega" (Rev. 1:8)
35. "They were ____ afraid" (Mark 9:6)
36. "I am the ____:. . .if any man enter in, he shall be saved" (John 10:9)

40. Effects, abbr.
41. "Emmanuel, which being interpreted is, _____ with us" (Matt. 1:23)
44. "I will give unto thee the _____ of the kingdom" (Matt. 16:19)
46. Nashville's state, abbr.
47. "Why make ye this _____, and weep" (Mark 5:39)
49. "I seek not mine _____ will, but the will of the Father" (John 5:30)
50. Vagrancy, abbr.
51. Large body of water
52. Nurse, abbr.

PUZZLE 9

ACROSS

1. "A ____ that needeth not to be ashamed" (2 Tim. 2:15)
6. "The word of God. . .is sharper than any twoedged ____" (Heb. 4:12)
10. Friend, Fr.
11. When you will arrive, approximately, abbr.
12. In favor of
13. Belonging to God's chose nation
15. Young lady, Fr., abbr.
17. Man's name
19. Sons of Judah, Er and ____ (Gen. 46:12)
21. Edward, for short
23. Chinese dynasty
24. Firstborn son of Judah (Gen. 38:2–3)
27. Primps
29. "____ not yourselves" (Rom. 12:19)
31. "When the morning stars ____" (Job 38:7)
32. "Jesus thou ____ of God" (Matt. 8:29)
33. Letter before "em"
34. Teletypewriter, abbr.
35. In order that
37. Small particle
39. Translation, abbr.
41. Son of Adam
43. Prophet during David's reign
46. Masculine article, Fr.
47. Indicate agreement with a movement of the head
48. "These ____ Milcah did bear" (Gen. 22:23)
50. Letter after "em"
52. Preposition
53. "Lion will not ____ himself" (Isa. 31:4)
55. Sea lettuce
57. "____ obtained favor" (Esther 2:15)
58. Moisten

DOWN

1. "As ____ as snow" (Rev. 1:14)
2. "A ____ thing" (Dan. 2:11)
3. Department store chain
4. Appearance
5. Sea monster of loch
6. America's uncle
7. "____ the ears, but he heareth not" (Isa. 42:20)
8. Transportation on tracks, abbr.
9. "Let us not be weary in well ____" (Gal 6:9)
14. "____ my people go" (Exod. 5:1)
16. Brief periods of time
18. Hills
20. Response, abbr.
22. "I. . .beheld your ____, I found an altar with this inscription, To The Unknown God" (Acts 17:23)
25. City in Nevada
26. "Delivered when she was past ____" (Heb. 11:11)
28. "Take it, and ____ it up" (Rev. 10:9)
29. Josaphat's father (Matt. 1:8)
30. Building wing
35. To stow, especially in a ship's hold
36. Exclamation
38. St. Paul is the capital of this state, abbr.
39. Not that

40. "The heathen ____" (Ps. 46:6)
42. Masculine article, Sp.
44. "Lest he ____ my soul like a
    lion" (Ps. 7:2)
45. New England state, abbr.
47. "As it was in the days of ____,
    so shall it be also in the days of
    the Son of man" (Luke 17:26)
49. Stomach, for short
51. Girl's name
53. Syllable of satisfaction
54. Exist
56. Low pressure, abbr.

by Cheryl Keiser

PUZZLE 10

ACROSS

1. "Divided the light from the ____" (Gen. 1:4)
8. "He causeth his wind to ____" (Ps. 147:18)
12. Indiana State University, abbr.
13. Angers
14. "Sat upon ____ of them" (Acts 2:3)
15. Village, abbr.
16. "The earth brought forth ____" (Gen. 1:12)
18. Nazareth College and Academy, abbr.
19. Chemical suffix
20. Eastern seaboard state
21. "Being understood by the things that are made, even his ____ power" (Rom. 1:20)
25. Iron, chem. symbol
26. 9th through 12th grades, abbr.
27. "Let my people ____" (Exod. 5:1)
28. "Voice ____ like the sea" (Jer. 6:23 NAS)
30. "And darkness was upon the face of the ____" (Gen. 1:2)
32. "In the beginning ____" (Gen. 1:1)
34. Son of Peleg (Gen. 11:18)
35. "God called the light ____" (Gen. 1:5)
36. "Yielding ____ after his kind" (Gen. 1:12)
37. "____ I have done this" (Ps. 7:3)
39. Fifty-four, Rom. num.
40. "Thou mayest freely ____" (Gen. 2:16)
41. "She took some and ____ it" (Gen. 3:6 NIV)
42. Articles

44. "____ that may fly above the earth" (Gen. 1:20)
47. "Thou shalt ____ eat of it" (Gen. 2:17)
48. "Let there be ____ in the firmament" (Gen. 1:14)
50. "Planted a garden in the ____" (Gen. 2:8 NIV)
52. Fellow of Entomology Society, abbr.
53. American Association of University Professors, abbr.
55. "The ____ was without form" (Gen. 1:2)
56. "And the ____ yielding fruit" (Gen. 1:12)

DOWN

1. "God ____ the light from the darkness" (Gen. 1:4)
2. "I will now turn ____, and see" (Exod. 3:3)
3. "The greater light to ____ the day" (Gen. 1:16)
4. "And the darkness he called ____" (Gen. 1:5)
5. "A people that do ____ in their heart" (Ps. 95:10)
6. "Have dominion over the fish of the ____" (Gen. 1:26)
7. Selective Service System, abbr.
8. "Let there ____ light" (Gen. 1:3)
9. "Let the dry ____ appear" (Gen. 1:9)
10. Ozark Christian College, abbr.
11. "God created great ____" (Gen. 1:21)
17. "I saw a ____ fall from heaven" (Rev. 9:1)
21. Catch sight of
22. "Any taste in the white of an ____" (Job 6:6)

23. Rest, as a bird
24. "And the _____ God planted" (Gen. 2:8)
25. "And the _____ of righteousness is sown in peace" (James 3:18)
26. "Thus the _____ and the earth were finished" (Gen. 2:1)
29. Of age, Lat. abbr.
31. Revise
33. Dover's state, abbr.
38. "The God which _____ me all my life" (Gen. 48:15)
39. "The moving creature that hath _____" (Gen. 1:20)
40. Suffix meaning to the utmost degree

41. "Thou shalt make an _____" (Exod. 30:1)
43. "Why beholdest thou the _____" (Matt. 7:3)
44. "_____ which we did eat in Egypt" (Num. 11:5)
45. King of Bashan (Num. 21:33)
46. "Said unto the woman, _____ is this?" (Gen. 3:13)
48. "_____ there be light" (Gen. 1:3)
49. "If any man will _____ thee" (Matt. 5:40)
51. Preposition
52. Romance language, abbr.
54. Sweaty class
by Rebecca Souder

PUZZLE 11

ACROSS

1. "There was a marriage in ____ of Galilee" (John 2:1)
5. Headwear
8. "When they saw the ____, they rejoiced" (Matt. 2:10)
12. Son of Jerameel (1 Chron. 2:25)
13. "If we confess ____ sins" (1 John 1:9)
14. "Her ____ shall be holiness to the Lord" (Isa. 23:18)
15. Mexican money
16. Suffix meaning "process or function"
17. "For I have slain ____ ____" (Gen. 4:23) (2 words)
18. "Thou hast made us to drink the wine of ____" (Ps. 60:3)
21. "The archers ____ him" (1 Sam. 31:3)
22. Shoe width
23. "It shall be health to thy ____" (Prov. 3:8)
26. Girl's name
27. "That I may ____ Christ" (Phil. 3:8)
30. "It shall be a statute for ____" (Lev. 23:31)
31. "Samuel arose, and ____ him up from Gilgal" (1 Sam. 13:15)
32. Son of Zerah (1 Chron. 2:6)
33. Money owed the government
34. "____ also the Jairite was a chief ruler about David" (2 Sam. 20:26)
35. "Thou shalt call his name ____: for he shall save his people from their sins" (Matt. 1:21)
36. Onassis
37. "Babylon is taken, ____ is confounded" (Jer. 50:2)
38. "To ____ of goods, or to imprisonment" (Ezra 7:26)
44. "There was also ____ ____ for the tribe of Manasseh" (Josh. 17:1) (2 words)
45. Place for experiments
46. "Strain at a ____" (Matt. 23:24)
48. Belonging to me
49. Compass point
50. Prefix for half
51. Not rich
52. Of the, Sp.
53. Very, Fr.

DOWN

1. Police officer (slang)
2. Vicinity
3. Scottish lake
4. "There arose ____ generation after them" (Judg. 2:10)
5. "____ it all joy" (James 1:2)
6. Comb. form for ear
7. "Now therefore ____ yourselves before the Lord" (1 Sam. 10:19)
8. "How long will you turn my glory into ____?" (Ps. 4:2)
9. "In harvest ____ thou shalt rest" (Exod. 34:21)
10. Brother of Uz (1 Chron. 1:42)
11. "A great and strong wind ____ the mountains" (1 Kings 19:11)
19. "They. . .their lamps, and took no ____ with them" (Matt. 25:3)
20. "Even as a ____ gathereth her chickens" (Matt. 23:37)
23. "For he shall pluck my feet out of the ____" (Ps. 25:15)
24. "And the king of Assyria brought men from Babylon. . . and from ____" (2 Kings 17:24)

25. "For they ____ you with their wiles" (Num. 25:18)
26. Auto club, abbr.
27. "And the child ____ cured" (Matt. 17:18)
28. First son of Caleb (1 Chron. 4:15)
29. Naval Air Station, abbr.
31. "The rams . . .are ringstraked. . . and ____" (Gen. 31:12)
32. "But his ____ is in the law of the Lord" (Ps. 1:2)
34. A son of Bela (1 Chron. 7:7)
35. Type of airplane
36. "They returned from searching of the land ____ forty days" (Num. 13:25)

37. "And the beginning of his [Nimrod's] kingdom was ____ " (Gen. 10:10)
38. "I will ____ against thee" (Isa. 29:3)
39. Miscellaneous mixture
40. Something forbidden
41. "Sweet ____ from a far country" (Jer. 6:20)
42. Latin prefix meaning "burden"
43. "Ye might have life through his ____" (John 20:31)
47. Poetic contraction for "it is"

by Janet W. Adkins

PUZZLE 12

ACROSS

1. Christian disciple from Joppa who was known for her charity (Acts 9:36–43)
6. Resurrection day
10. Sixth Jewish month (Neh. 6:15)
11. Jesus did not give this to Pilate (John 19:9)
12. In the direction of
13. Derisive wit that attacks evil
15. A priest placed blood on the tips of these (Lev. 14:14)
18. Dog noise
19. Laughter noise
20. "The valley of the shadow of ____" (Ps. 23:4)
21. Live
22. Noah's boat
24. What John did to the little book given to him by the angel (Rev. 10:10)
25. Eagle (Lev. 11:18)
27. The son of Ikkesh (2 Sam. 23:26)
28. Expressing gratitude
31. Ceremonial act
32. "Wilt thou break a ____ driven to and fro?" (Job 13:25)
33. In order that
35. Up to now
36. "May be able to comprehend with all saints what is the ____, and length, and depth, and height" (Eph. 3:18)
39. "This is the ____ which the Lord hath made" (Ps. 118:24)
41. Absence or closure of a natural body passage
44. "I shall ____ thee wisdom" (Job 33:33)
46. The Lord makes us do this in green pastures
48. To act properly
50. "____ Lord God! behold, thou hast made the heaven and earth" (Jer. 32:17)
51. "They sought to ____ hold on him" (Mark 12:12)
52. Edward, for short
53. One does this on the seventh day of the week
54. Feminine pronoun

DOWN

1. Dover is the capital of this state, abbr.
2. Old Latin, abbr.
3. Moabite woman from whom Christ was descended
4. Jesus ascended up to heaven in one of these
5. A day of rest and worship
6. Curved shape
7. Gone
8. Animal or plant bristle
9. Voyage
14. Son of Salah and grandson of Shem (Gen. 10:24)
15. "The child Jesus ____ behind in Jerusalem" (Luke 2:43)
16. "His ____ was locusts" (Matt. 3:4)
17. "For every one that ____ shall be cut off" (Zech. 5:3)
19. Esau was, but Jacob wasn't
21. Pleads
23. Part of the children of Zebulun's inheritance (Josh. 19:15–16)
25. "Covet earnestly the best ____" (1 Cor. 12:31)
26. Opposite of out

29. "The day of the Lord is ____"
    (Obad. 1:15)
30. Location of the water of Meribah
    (Num. 27:14)
34. Amorite king (Deut. 31:4)
37. Contests of speed
38. "The mountains and the ____
    shall break forth before you into
    singing" (Isa. 55:12)
40. Paul continued a ____ and a half
    at Corinth (Acts 18:11)
42. The father of Rizpah, Saul's
    concubine (2 Sam. 3:7)
43. President Lincoln, for short
45. Address abbreviation

47. "Mine ____ affecteth mine
    heart" (Lam. 3:51)
49. Edwin for short
50. In this way

by Janet W. Adkins

PUZZLE 13

ACROSS

1. King of Judah (Isa. 38:1)
7. Son of Jacob
10. Four, Rom. num.
11. While in Antioch, this man predicted a famine (Acts 11:27–28)
12. "At Antioch there were prophets and teachers: Barnabas, Simeon. . . , Lucius of Cyrene, ____ and Saul" (Acts 13:1 NIV)
14. This king destroyed and burned an idol his mother had made (1 Kings 15:13)
16. Don't fight like a man beating this (1 Cor. 9:26)
17. For example, Lat. abbr.
18. Ancestor of Saul and the son of Benjamin (1 Sam. 9:1)
20. God's name for Himself, I ____
21. "Will your ____ talk reduce men to silence?" (Job 11:3 NIV)
23. "A man of ____ spirit gains honor" (Prov. 29:23 NIV)
25. Cathode, abbr.
27. Southern state, abbr.
28. "The ____ shall eat straw like the ox" (Isa. 11:7)
30. Pertaining to urinary tract, prefix
31. "The body is a ____, though it is made up of many parts" (1 Cor. 12:12 NIV)
32. The man who lost both his inheritance and his blessing to his brother (Gen. 27:30–40)
33. Succeeded Ahaziah as king (2 Kings 1:17 NIV)
35. Nautical measure of speed, abbr.
36. Harry's nickname
38. First month of autumn, abbr.
40. One of the border towns of the children of Naphtali (Josh. 19:32–33)
43. "Their feet ____ into sin" (Isa. 59:7 NIV)
45. Article
46. Belonging to a priest in Midian who had seven daughters (Exod. 2:11–3:1)

49. "The ____ is already at the root" (Matt. 3:10 NIV)
50. Alternate spelling for 15 down
51. Greek word for "my God" (Matt. 27:46 NIV)
53. Shipbuilder and zookeeper
55. A prophet and book of the Old Testament
56. Dorm helper, abbr.
57. Collection of sayings
59. New Testament prophetess (Luke 2:36)
60. "Cancel any ____ your brother owes" (Deut. 15:3 NIV)
62. Old Testament book that follows Ezra
65. "Better a ____ of vegetables where there is love" (Prov. 15:17)
67. "Let the dead ____ their dead" (Luke 9:60)
68. A book of the Pentateuch, abbr.
70. This man lived and died, but he was never born
72. "____, follow me" (Matt. 4:19 NIV)
73. This man disagreed with a great fish
74. A son of Noah (Gen. 5:32)

DOWN

1. Prophet of Judah and book of the Old Testament
2. King who went into the citadel of the palace and set it on fire, dying there (1 Kings 16:18)
3. Peron's first name
4. "Let us make man in our ____" (Gen. 1:26)
5. False prophet who took the yoke off Jeremiah's neck and broke it (Jer. 28:10)
6. Sent to David to rebuke him and expose his sin (2 Sam. 12:1–10)
7. Father of all who play the harp or the flute (Gen. 4:21)
8. America, abbr.
9. Amnon was killed by him for raping Tamar (2 Sam. 13:1–29)
13. Girl's name
15. Youngest of the Little Women

19. "Ye know neither the day nor the
    ____" (Matt. 25:13)
22. A Reubenite who was swallowed
    up by the earth (Num. 16:27–32)
24. A gentle answer turns this away
    (Prov. 15:1)
26. The daughter of Phanuel
    (Luke 2:36)
28. Library science, abbr.
29. Old uncial, abbr.
32. The man who went to heaven in a
    fiery chariot
33. Nebat's son (2 Chron. 10:15)
34. Great work
37. Be, first person singular,
    present tense
39. Giant killed by David
41. Defendent's adversary, abbr.
42. Article
44. Esther and Mordecai's enemy
47. Printer's measure

48. Father of Abraham (Gen. 11:27)
51. An elder who prophesied with
    Medad (Num. 11:26)
52. Globe
53. Book of the Old Testament that
    follows Micah
54. "Give bread unto thine ____"
    (Judg. 8:6)
55. One of the Gospels, abbr.
58. Mountain where Moses died
61. Son of Baasha (1 Kings 16:8)
63. Before, poetic
64. Past
66. "Take him to the . . .doorpost and
    pierce his ____ with an awl"
    (Exod. 21:6 NIV)
68. Father, dial Brit
69. Used to indicate ordinal numbers
71. Common graduate degree, abbr.
    by Elizabeth B. Smith

PUZZLE 14

ACROSS

1. "I ____ not want" (Ps. 23:1)
6. "The sucking child shall play on the hole of the ____" (Isa. 11:8)
9. Father of Hophni and Phinehas (1 Sam. 2:27, 34)
10. "Lie down in green ____" (Ps. 23:2)
14. "Then I will ____ your flesh" (Judg. 8:7)
16. "____ the people together" (Deut. 33:17)
17. Mother, for short
19. Sandwich shops
21. Maiden name
22. "I will fear no ____" (Ps. 23:4)
24. "All the days of my ____" (Ps. 23:6)
26. "He will not ____ thee" (Deut. 31:8)
28. "Thy rod and thy staff they____ me" (Ps. 23:4)
31. "Thou preparest a ____ before me" (Ps. 23:5)
34. Yukon Front, abbr.
35. Mined matter
37. "Even unto the ____ of the jubile" (Lev. 27:18)
38. "Lord, be not ____ from me" (Ps. 35:22)
40. What?
42. "Thy ____ and thy staff" (Ps. 23:4)
44. "Valley of the shadow of ____" (Ps. 23:4)
46. "None that doeth good, no not ____" (Ps. 14:3)
47. Maryland's neighbor to the south, abbr.
49. Flightless bird

51. "In ____ time Christ died for the ungodly" (Rom. 5:6)
54. "To lie down in ____ pastures" (Ps. 23:2)
57. Assistant, abbr.
59. Not Jr.
60. Edible root
61. Inhabitant

DOWN

2. "____ maketh me to lie down" (Ps. 23:2)
3. Height, abbr.
4. "____ down in green pastures" (Ps. 23:2)
5. Organization for veterans, abbr.
6. Preposition indicating when or where
7. "I. . .will ____ with him, and he with me" (Rev. 3:20)
8. Fruit
10. "Thou ____ a table before me" (Ps. 23:5)
11. "Beside the ____ waters" (Ps. 23:2)
12. Wind direction
13. "The Lord is my ____" (Ps. 23:1)
15. In the year of our Lord, Lat. abbr.
17. "____ shall follow me" (Ps. 23:6)
18. Audio-visual, abbr.
20. Yes, Sp.
23. "____ ____ hath sent me unto you" (Exod. 3:14) (2 words)
25. "____ their skin from off them" (Mic. 3:3)
26. "Fear no evil: ____ thou art with me" (Ps. 23:4)
27. "God saw that ___ was good" (Gen. 1:10)

29. Not on

30. "Dwell in the house of the Lord _____ _____" (Ps. 23:6) (2 words)

32. "The well. . .is between Kadesh and _____" (Gen. 16:14)

33. Southeast Asian

36. Myself

39. Paid announcement

41. "I will dwell in the _____ of the Lord" (Ps. 23:6)

43. Medium, abbr.

45. "Annointest my _____ with oil" (Ps. 23:5)

48. "Thou _____ with me" (Ps. 23:4)

50. Social worker's graduate degree

52. "_____ not vain repetitions" (Matt. 6:7)

53. "Do not _____, my beloved brethren" (James 1:16)

55. Apiece, abbr.

56. "I will fear _____ evil" (Ps. 23:4)

58. Thallium, chem. symbol

by Elizabeth B. Smith

PUZZLE 15

ACROSS

1. "Ye are the _____ of the earth" (Matt. 5:13)
5. Peter healed this man who had been bedridden with palsy for eight years (Acts 9:33–34)
9. "I am _____ your pillows" (Ezek. 13:20)
10. "_____, I am with you alway" (Matt. 28:20)
11. Og's bed was made of this (Deut. 3:11)
12. Set apart for worship
16. Edward's nickname
17. A camel has one
18. Quality, suffix
19. "It shall return, and shall be eaten: as a _____ tree" (Isa. 6:13)
21. Presently
23. "Strain at a gnat, and swallow a _____" (Matt. 23:24)
26. "Go to the _____, thou sluggard" (Prov. 6:6)
27. Noah's son
28. "Listen, O _____, unto me" (Isa. 49:1)
31. A magistrate of ancient Rome
33. A case for holding small articles
34. The second note of the musical scale
36. Nickel, chem. symbol
37. "That we may _____ our hearts, unto wisdom" (Ps. 90:12)
38. "I will _____ thee and teach thee" (Ps. 32:8)
41. Not off
42. Winged mammal
43. Kentucky's neighbor, abbr.
44. "The twenty-four _____ fall down before him" (Rev. 4:10 NIV)
48. "Rejoice not against me, O mine _____" (Mic. 7:8)
50. Step
51. I
52. "Lips of wise _____ knowledge" (Prov. 15:7)

DOWN

1. "Salute every _____ in Christ" (Phil. 4:21)
2. "_____ with thine adversary" (Matt. 5:25)
3. John sent his Revelation to this church in Asia Minor (Rev. 1:11)
4. "_____. . .that may abide the fire" (Num. 31:22–23)
5. "And hereby we know that we are of the truth, and shall _____ our hearts before him" (1 John 3:19)
6. Where Samson lived after he slaughtered the Philistines (Judg. 15:8, 11)
7. "He that hath an _____, let him hear" (Rev. 2:7)
8. Paul wrote one of his epistles to these people
13. Compound, abbr.
14. Seventh letter of the Greek alphabet
15. Succession of rulers from the same descent
20. "Kings of the earth shall. . . _____" (Rev. 18:9)
22. Activated
24. Spring-flowering bush with fragrant blossoms
25. Twelfth letter of the alphabet
27. "The Son of man shall be betrayed unto the chief priests and unto the _____" (Matt. 20:18)

29. Groups of seven
30. Elongated fish
32. Soiled
35. The father of Ahira (Num. 1:15)
39. "And there shall come forth a rod out of the _____ of Jesse" (Isa. 11:1)
40. Not, prefix
41. Either
45. "One went out into the field to gather herbs,. . .and gathered thereof wild gourds his _____ full" (2 Kings 4:39)

46. What would happen to Adam and Eve if they ate the forbidden fruit
47. "The wayfaring men. . .shall not _____" (Isa. 35:8)
49. "Come unto _____, all ye that labour" (Matt. 11:28)
50. Silicon, chem. symbol

PUZZLE 16

ACROSS

1. "A stormy wind shall ____ it" (Ezek. 13:11)
5. "Jonah was gone down ____ the sides of the ship" (Jon. 1:5)
9. Ration
12. "My cup runneth ____" (Ps. 23:5)
13. "Every one had ____ faces" (Ezek. 1:6)
14. "A vineyard of ____ wine" (Isa. 27:2)
15. Prevent
17. To be announced, abbr.
18. "Nathan the prophet and Shimei, and ____" (1 Kings 1:8)
19. "Prince of the power of the ____" (Eph. 2:2)
21. "Neither will I ____ an offering at your hand" (Mal. 1:10)
23. "Those virgins arose, and ____ their lamps" (Matt. 25:7)
27. "The ____ was come to the place of the arrow" (1 Sam. 20:37)
28. Charged particles
29. The disciple who denied Christ
31. Interrogatory syllable
33. "I have stretched out my hand, and no ____ regarded" (Prov. 1:24)
34. "Number all the firstborn of the ____" (Num. 3:40)
35. Fruit drink
36. "The children of Gad called the altar ____" (Josh. 22:34)
37. "But ye are a chosen generation, a ____ priesthood" (1 Pet. 2:9)
38. Colored layer of the eye
39. "A third part shall be at the gate of ____" (2 Kings 11:6)
40. December 31
42. "They shall take up a lamentation for thee, and ____ over thee" (Ezek. 27:32)
45. Cup
46. "____, even the ancient high places are our's in possession" (Ezek. 36:2)
47. Anger
49. "____, Mahalaleel, Jered" (1 Chron. 1:2)
53. "Bring unto thee pure ____ olive beaten for the light" (Lev. 24:2)
54. "I went down into the garden of ____ to see the fruits of the valley" (Song of Sol. 6:11)
56. "He went into a city called ____" (Luke 7:11)
57. Sun, Sp.
58. Equipment
59. "And came to the strong hold of ____" (2 Sam. 24:7)

DOWN

1. "Thy ____ and thy staff they comfort me" (Ps. 23:4)
2. "The serpent beguiled ____" (2 Cor. 11:3)
3. "The fishes that are taken in an evil ____" (Eccles. 9:12)
4. "The diviners. . .have told false ____" (Zech. 10:2)
5. "____ they shall enter into my rest" (Heb. 4:3)
6. "____ by might, nor by power" (Zech. 4:6)
7. Large wind instrument
8. "Unto them were committed the ____ of God" (Rom. 3:2)
9. "Cause me to understand wherein I have ____" (Job 6:24)
10. "____ thou not silence" (Ps. 83:1)
11. Blue-pencil
16. Edge
20. "I will ____ it" (Philem. 19)
22. Auto
23. "I set him a ____" (Neh. 2:6)
24. "Whither have ye made a ____ to day" (1 Sam. 27:10)
25. "There was no room for them in the ____" (Luke 2:7)
26. "Thou shalt no ____ to offer the first of thy ripe fruits" (Exod. 22:29)

30. "Ziph, and ____, and Bealoth" (Josh. 15:24)
31. First garden
32. "Hairs of your ____ are all numbered" (Luke 12:7)
34. "Thou shalt seek me in the ____" (Job 7:21)
35. Latin expression of greeting
37. "Ye tithe mint and ____ and all manner of herbs" (Luke 11:42)
38. "The king's commandment was ____" (Dan. 3:22)
39. "I am ____ and despised" (Ps. 119:141)
41. Diving bird
42. East Asian country

43. "Uzzah and ____, the sons of Abinadab" (2 Sam. 6:3)
44. "That was the ____ Light" (John 1:9)
48. Approximate time of arrival, abbr.
50. "I tell you ____; but rather division" (Luke 12:51)
51. "Meet the Lord in the ____" (1 Thess. 4:17)
52. Compass point
55. Twelfth-grader, abbr.

by Evelyn M. Boyington

ACROSS

1. To damage
4. "And Saul ____ unto David" (1 Sam. 17:37)
8. Cushions
12. "Blessed ____ the meek" (Matt. 5:5)
13. Son of Helem (1 Chron. 7:35)
14. Operatic solo
15. ____ ____ Goliath (2 words)
17. Genuine
18. Genesis garden
19. ____ ____ of Two Cities (2 words)
20. "The wine ____ ____" (Ps. 75:8) (2 words)
22. Man of brave deeds
24. Female rabbits
25. Sealing wax
29. Epoch
30. Member of the nobility
31. Anger
32. "Making a noise with psalteries ____ ____" (1 Chron. 15:28) (2 words)
34. "They ____ not the bones till the morrow" (Zeph. 3:3)
35. "The ____ are a people not strong" (Prov. 30:25)
36. "Yet offend in one ____" (James 2:10)
37. "The ____ of his fire shall not shine" (Job 18:5)
40. "____! for that day is great" (Jer. 30:7)
41. "The ____ of the Lord was with him" (Luke 1:66)
42. David's friend
46. Father of Shammah (2 Sam. 23:11)
47. Son of Jerahmeel (1 Chron. 2:25)
48. Female sheep
49. "Thou shalt not build it of ____ stone" (Exod. 20:25)
50. Wagers
51. Fourth letter of the alphabet

DOWN

1. "Lo, ye see the man is ____" (1 Sam. 21:14)
2. Son of Jether (1 Chron. 7:38)
3. Pastor's title
4. Having walls
5. "There was ____ ____ sent from God" (John 1:6) (2 words)
6. "There was no room for them in the ____" (Luke 2:7)
7. Father
8. "And he was in the hinder ____ ____ the ship" (Mark 4:38) (2 words)
9. Length x width
10. Knob
11. Garage ____
16. The ____ of March
19. Son of Dishan (1 Chron. 1:42)
20. Thought
21. "As ____ as I had eaten it, my belly was bitter" (Rev. 10:10)
22. "We hanged our ____ upon the willows" (Ps. 137:2)
23. Greek god of love
25. "For we know in ____" (1 Cor. 13:9)
26. "He said, It is ____" (John 19:30)
27. Teheran's country
28. Salamander
30. "Behold, I stood upon the ____ of the river" (Gen. 41:17)

by Elaine Okupski

33. "____ not your hearts" (Heb. 3:8)
34. "He shall bring a she ____ of the first year for a sin offering" (Num. 15:27)
36. Schemes
37. Middle eastern ruler
38. Book leaf
39. "____ ____ heart also will I give you" (Ezek. 36:26) (2 words)
40. "Casting ____ ____ into the sea" (Mark 1:16) (2 words)
42. Old Testament book
43. Metal-bearing rock
44. "Stand in ____, and sin not" (Ps. 4:4)
45. Born, Fr.

ACROSS

1. "Give ear, O ____ of Israel" (Ps. 80:1)
8. Animal fat
11. "And now abideth faith, ____, charity" (1 Cor. 13:13)
12. "Every ____ shall be filled, and every mountain and hill shall be brought low" (Luke 3:5)
14. Gold, chem. symbol
15. Revise
17. Direction
18. Dental surgeon, abbr.
19. "Make the ____ for fire" (Ezek. 24:9)
20. Advantage, resource
22. Over (poetic)
24. Father
26. What the doctor wants you to say when you open your mouth
27. "To him. . .who liveth for ____" (Rev. 4:9)
30. "They shall fall, and ____ rise" (Amos 8:14)
33. Abijam's son (1 Kings 15:8)
34. Foreign
36. A cereal grain
37. Three letters of Latin anagram for Christ
38. Chemical warfare, abbr.
39. Old Testament, abbr.
40. Longing
42. Land measurement
44. Larger, abbr.
46. "The four and twenty elders, which sat before God on their ____" (Rev. 11:16)
48. A snake-shaped fish
49. "The veil of the temple was ____ in the midst" (Luke 23:45)
51. Paul was a ____-maker

53. Building wing
54. "What then? are we ____ than they?" (Rom. 3:9)
56. "He shall suck the poison of ____" (Job 20:16)
58. Exclamation of disgust
59. "Cattle shall feed in large ____" (Isa. 30:23)

DOWN

1. "Put your trust in my ____ (Judg. 9:15)
2. "Peace be to thine ____" (1 Sam. 25:6)
3. Estimated position, abbr.
4. Chick's sound
5. "Turn ye from your ____ ways" (Ezek. 33:11)
6. Scored
7. 550, Rom. num.
8. Part of an eye or a camera
9. Affirmative votes
10. "Deliver our lives from ____" (Josh. 2:13)
13. "Narrow is the way, which ____ unto life" (Matt. 7:14)
16. "Pharisee besought him to ____" (Luke 11:37)
21. "He that hath an ____, let him hear" (Rev. 2:7)
23. "Elias verily cometh first, and ____ all things" (Mark 9:12)
25. "I am the God of Bethel, where thou ____ the pillar" (Gen. 31:13)
28. Very large
29. Color again
31. Passport
32. European Community, abbr.
33. Alcoholics Anonymous, abbr.
35. Inhabits

36. "Hurt not the wine and the
    ____" (Rev. 6:6)
38. Crawls
41. "Take, ____; this is my body"
    (Matt. 26:26)
43. Common Era, abbr.
45. Gregory, for short
46. "There is but a ____ between me
    and death" (1 Sam. 20:3)
47. Tin, chem. symbol
50. New Testament, abbr.
52. Black sticky material
54. Abbreviation for a dry measure
55. Royal Academy, abbr.
57. Direction

PUZZLE 19

ACROSS

1. Detestable, disgusting (Prov. 3:32)
8. Dishonest person, a cheat (Isa. 32:5)
12. A unit of measure, just less than two quarts (2 Kings 6:25 KJV)
13. "Also the ____ and the bear will graze" (Isa. 11:7)
15. The Peach state, abbr.
16. Sharp instrument (Josh. 5:2–3)
18. Passover (Acts 12:4 KJV)
21. Allow (Ps. 119:10)
23. The Lord turned this river into blood using Moses' staff (Exod. 7:20–21)
25. The body of writing that describes the new covenant between God and man, abbr.
26. "Speaking out arrogant words of ____" (2 Pet. 2:18)
27. Book of the Apocrypha
28. Often a symbol of refreshment and blessing in the dry summers of Palestine (Deut. 32:2)
29. "As far as the east is from the ____" (Ps. 103:12)
31. An image of a false god (Exod. 20:4)
32. Hebrew word for house; also second letter of the Hebrew alphabet
33. Unit of weight, abbr.
34. "The Word of God enlightens the ____" (Ps. 19:8)
35. "And takes a cypress or an ____" (Isa. 44:14)
36. The oldest son of Elpaal, a Benjamite (1 Chron. 8:12)
38. Piece of clothing to wear on the upper body
40. David's book of poetry, abbr.
41. "Do not ____ meaningless repetition" (Matt. 6:7)
42. "Surely in a night, ____ of Moab is devastated and ruined" (Isa. 15:1)
43. Amos denounces Israel for its use of this (Amos 3:15 & 6:4)
44. A trap (Ps. 140:5 KJV)
46. Grandfather of the prophet Zechariah (Zech. 1:1, 7)

48. Grandson of Boaz, father of David (Ruth 4:22)
49. "Altars to ____ were built in Palestine, thanks to Jezebel and Athalia" (1 Kings 16:31–32)
52. An Israelite who took a garment, silver, and gold from the spoil at Jericho (Josh. 7:21)
53. "____ them around your neck" (Prov. 6:21)
56. Health Management Organization, abbr.
57. "Reduced Sodom and Gomorrah to ____" (2 Pet. 2:6)
58. ____ Nebo, abbr.
59. Roman colony (Acts 16:8)
61. Preposition that indicates position
62. We are this through Christ (Gal. 4:1)
64. "Received the linen ____" (2 Chron. 1:16 KJV)
65. "God shall ____ to him the plagues" (Rev. 22:18)
66. Imitate
68. "____ to speak" (James 1:19)
70. Isaiah compared Israel's despoiling to robbing one of these (Isa. 10:14)
71. Second son of Noah (Gen. 5:32)
72. Deception took its first hold on humanity here
73. Do not let this go down on your anger (Eph. 4:26)

DOWN

1. "See fit to ____ God" (Rom. 1:28)
2. A Levite who sealed the covenant (Neh. 10:13)
3. A camel driver, keeper of King David's camels (1 Chron. 27:30)
4. "He casts forth his ____ as fragments" (Ps. 147:17)
5. "The city of the God ____-Amon" (Nah. 3:8)
6. "Stand in ____ of him" (Ps. 33:8)
7. Longing, intense desire (Matt. 5:28)
9. "The cities of ____" (Josh. 13:21)
10. Area in Palestine (Isa. 9:1)
11. Paul restored his life after he fell out of a window (Acts 20:9)
14. Disclosure of something previously unknown (Gal. 1:12)

17. Shackles for the feet (Prov. 7:22)
19. One who usurps Christ's name (1 John 2:22)
20. "But whenever _____ flesh appears on him, he shall be unclean" (Lev. 13:14)
22. And, Lat.
24. "Shall be _____ to separate us from the love of God" (Rom. 8:39)
28. "God may open up to us a _____ for the Word" (Col. 4:3)
30. Grow less
37. Custodian of royal harems (Dan. 1:3–18)
38. Continent in the southern hemisphere, abbr.
39. A chamber for deceased bodies (Matt. 27:60)
40. The Great Sphinx stands guard over this
45. Person from a non-Jewish nation (Matt. 6:7)

47. Divine nature (Col. 2:9)
48. With Jesus at the transfiguration (Matt. 17:1–8)
50. Exclamation of satisfaction
51. The capital city of Great Britain
52. Led the singing and sounded the cymbol; credited to him (Ps. 50 & 78–83)
54. "Watchful" (Num. 26:36)
55. "One _____ disobedience" (Rom. 5:19)
60. A prince known as a raven of the Midianites; was beheaded (Judg. 7:24–25)
63. Jacob used this to change the color of Laban's goats (Gen. 30:37–41)
65. This animal saw an angel (Num. 22:23)
66. Preposition used in similes
67. Electrical engineer, abbr.
69. Ourselves

by Michael J. Landi
(NASB)

PUZZLE 20

ACROSS

1. God told Adam and Eve to be fruitful and ____ (Gen. 1:22)
8. Without, Fr.
12. What Samuel does to Saul to show he'll be Israel's king
13. Clothing that covers the back
14. The prodigal son almost ate their food (Luke 15:16)
15. "____ not at all; neither by heaven; for it is God's throne" (Matt. 5:34)
17. A metal burned by fire (Num. 31:22–23)
18. Eleven, Rom. num.
20. "I am Alpha and the Omega, beginning and the ____" (Rev. 22:13)
21. Ma's husband
22. To trap
24. Gideon saw men lapping water like this animal (Judg. 7:5)
26. Address abbreviation
27. A rough rock where the eagle dwells (Job 39:27–28)
29. At the end of the world we will hear about these and rumors of these (Matt. 24:6)
32. Large feline
34. Dover is the capital of this state, abbr.
35. A soft, lustrous fabric made by worms
38. Hebrew custom of allowing the poor to follow the reapers and gather grain
40. Jesus said not to speak these kind of words (Matt. 12:36)
41. The initials of the man who came up with the theory of relativity
42. After eight days, Jesus was circumcised and ____ (Luke 2:21)
45. Negative
46. Tensile strength, abbr.
47. To direct the course
48. Gideon hoped this would be wet, then dry
50. Exclamation of surprise
51. A name for Mother
52. Ourselves
53. Homonym of sew
54. A tall pasture grass
56. A printer's measure
57. A Levitical city in the hill country of Judah (Josh. 15:51)
58. Briefly lowers the head

DOWN

1. Ruler, lord, teacher (Matt. 8:19)
2. To reverse the winding
3. When you wear the armor of God, you should have your ____ girt with truth (Eph. 6:14)
4. A soft metal
5. Not exact
6. Two cups, abbr.
7. Life support system, abbr.
8. "Yea, though I walk through the valley of the ____ of death" (Ps. 23:4)
9. Jesus spoke of the fowls of the ____ (Matt. 6:26)
10. Not rated, abbr.
11. Produces hot, moist air
13. "God. . .shall ____ his angel" (Gen. 24:7)
16. Us
19. Supply with water by artificial means
23. If we wait upon the Lord, we will mount up with wings like these birds

25. Seventh son of Jacob, firstborn of Zilpah (Gen. 30:11)
28. Word to make a horse turn to the right
30. What Christ did for us
31. Everything
33. "The Son of man came. . .to give his life a ____" (Matt. 20:28)
35. Marked by sin
36. "Little children, keep yourselves from ____" (1 John 5:21)
37. City in south Judah, conquered by Joshua in the northern campaign (Josh. 12:22)
39. Prophet during the reigns of David and Solomon

43. Myself
44. Persian coins (Ezra 2:69)
49. The sound of a dove
54. The opposite of stop
55. The article that precedes words beginning with a vowel

ACROSS

1. Greek letter used for the ratio of a circle's circumference to its diameter
3. Undergraduate degree, abbr.
5. David was king in ____ (2 Sam. 2:11)
9. Raises up
11. Organization for African Unity, abbr.
13. In regards to, abbr.
14. He made a vow with David (1 Sam. 18:3)
18. Girl's name
20. Stomach muscle, for short
21. A small building
22. Compass point
23. Jesse's youngest son (1 Sam. 16:11)
25. Regret
27. "If the Syrians be ____ strong for me" (2 Sam. 10:11)
28. Sense of who you are
29. Champion of the Philistines (1 Sam. 17:4)
31. Lieutenant, abbr.
32. The opposite of down
34. Six, Rom. num.
36. David used this to kill Goliath (1 Sam. 17:50)
39. Amount, abbr.
41. Woman's name
43. David's elder brother (1 Sam. 17:28)
44. A characteristic of David (1 Sam. 16:18)
47. "Drunk neither wine ____ strong drink" (1 Sam. 1:15)
49. A type of tree
50. Masculine article, Fr.
52. "Are not his sisters ____ with us?" (Mark 6:3)
53. His mother was Bathsheba (2 Sam. 12:24)
54. Resident, abbr.

DOWN

1. Nob was their city (1 Sam. 22:11)
2. That is, Lat. abbr.
3. Priests gave David hallowed ____ (1 Sam. 21:4)
4. Simile preposition
6. Period of time
7. Sheep's cries
8. A Moabite woman who was an ancestress of David and Jesus
10. "Thou ____ a virtuous woman" (Ruth 3:11)
12. The opposite of out
14. Saul threw it at David (1 Sam. 18:11)
15. Japanese sash
16. Not there
17. David escaped to this man's cave (1 Sam. 22:1)
19. "Herod. . .slew all the children. . . from ____ years old and under" (Matt. 2:16)
24. Wheeless vehicle
26. Electronic funds transfer, abbr.
28. That woman
30. Egg, prefix
33. David wrote many of these
35. David was in a ____ with Saul (1 Sam. 24:3)
37. "David made haste to ____ away" (1 Sam. 23:26)
38. "It was impossible for God to ____" (Heb. 6:18)
39. The captain of Saul's host (1 Sam. 14:50)

40. Sown among the wheat
    (Matt. 13:25)
42. Dekaliter, abbr.
45. "By him were ____ things
    created" (Col. 1:16)
46. New, recent, comb. form
48. Precious metal
51. "My word hath ____ place in
    you" (John 8:37)

by Elizabeth B. Smith

PUZZLE 22

ACROSS

1. "Blessed is the man that _____ not in the counsel of the ungodly" (Ps. 1:1)
7. "The ungodly shall not _____ in the judgment" (Ps. 1:5)
11. "Christ is the _____ of the church" (Eph. 5:23)
12. "Be like a tree planted by the _____ of water" (Ps. 1:3)
13. "A word spoken in _____ season, how good is it!" (Prov. 15:23)
14. Nest of an eagle or hawk
15. Preposition: toward
17. "Eyes have they, but they _____ not" (Ps. 115:5)
18. Took food
19. "All we like _____ have gone astray" (Isa. 53:6)
21. William, abbr.
22. Church, abbr.
23. Californian city, abbr.
24. "Nor _____ in the seat of the scornful" (Ps. 1:1)
27. Revise
29. It's capital is Indianapolis, abbr.
30. English Version, abbr.
31. Morning, abbr.
32. Vesicular exanthema, abbr.
33. Conjunction
34. "His _____ also shall not wither" (Ps. 1:3)
35. Elevated railroad
37. Alvin and Alan
38. Material at the bottom of the page, abbr.
40. "The Lord knoweth the way of the _____" (Ps. 1:6)
44. A cart for hire in India
45. National Guard, abbr.
47. Word to begin a question
48. To begin on a journey (2 words)
51. A telephone company, abbr.
52. "A tree. . .that bringeth forth his _____ in his season" (Ps. 1:3)

DOWN

1. "_____ he doeth shall prosper" (Ps. 1:3)
2. Initials of the man who wrote the equation E = MC2
3. "His delight is in the _____ of the Lord" (Ps. 1:2)
4. Boxing term, knocked down, abbr.
5. "I am the _____ vine" (John 15:1)
6. Go quickly
7. "Nor sitteth in the _____ of the scornful" (Ps. 1:1)
8. "And he shall be like a _____" (Ps. 1:3)
9. Airport surveillance radar, abbr.
10. "Whatsoever he _____ shall prosper" (Ps. 1:3)
13. Department, abbr.
16. Exclamation of surprise
17. "We shall all stand before the judgment _____ of Christ" (Rom. 14:10)
18. Amount, abbr.
20. "Therefore, _____ said unto Samuel, Go, lie down" (1 Sam. 3:9)
21. "The _____ driveth away" (Ps. 1:4)
22. "The godly are not so: but are like the _____" (Ps. 1:4)
24. "Nor standeth in the way of _____" (Ps. 1:1)
25. Gives a report
26. The nights before

28. "His ____ is in the law of the Lord" (Ps. 1:2)
36. Cozy talk
37. Gold, chemical symbol
39. "In his law doth he meditate day and ____" (Ps. 1:2)
41. Indian riverbank steps
42. Translation, abbr.
43. Public crier's word
45. Neither
46. Russian chief intelligence directorate, abbr.
47. Northwestern state, abbr.
49. Following, abbr.
50. Seventh note on the musical scale

ACROSS

1. Fiddling emperor
5. New Testament book
9. Noah's vessel
12. Dismounted
13. "For many _____ false witness against him" (Mark 14:56)
14. Gardening tool
15. "He shall not come _____ to offer the bread of his God" (Lev. 21:21)
16. "Every beast, every _____ thing, and every fowl" (Gen. 8:19)
18. Leah's second son (Gen. 30:12–13)
20. Actor James _____ Jones
21. "Then he that had received the five talents went and _____ with the same" (Matt. 25:16)
23. "There met him ten men that were lepers, which stood _____ off" (Luke 17:12)
27. Get a perfect score on a test
29. Result of sunbathing
30. "And Jacob _____ away unawares to Laban" (Gen. 31:20)
31. _____-man, scary childhood character
33. Son of Dishon (Gen. 36:26)
34. Rhythm and _____
35. "T" in PTL
36. Newsman Koppel
37. "My couch shall _____ my complaint" (Job 7:13)
38. Height of Noah's ark in cubits (Gen. 6:15)
40. Eastern garment
42. "And over the course of the second month was _____ an Ahohite" (1 Chron. 27:4)

45. "This is the token of the _____ which I have established" (Gen. 9:17)
49. Sudden attack
50. "And all went to be taxed, every _____ into his own city" (Luke 2:3)
51. Popular brand of sneakers
52. Biblical city
53. "But _____ unto you, scribes and Pharisees, hypocrites!" (Matt. 23:13)
54. "I am the Lord, and there is none _____" (Isa. 45:5)
55. Being, Lat.

DOWN

1. Common nickname for Grandmother
2. Belonging to inventor Whitney
3. "I am not come to call the _____, but sinners" (Matt. 9:13)
4. "The name of the one was Orpah, and the name of the _____ Ruth" (Ruth 1:4)
5. Beginning of the alphabet
6. To sway wildly
7. "Every place that the sole of your foot shall _____ upon" (Josh. 1:3)
8. Prophet
9. Son of Abdiel (1 Chron. 5:15)
10. Actor/director Howard
11. Small cask
17. "And thou shalt make a _____ of pure gold" (Exod. 28:36)
19. Gives a grade
22. "For this is the _____ of the Lord God of hosts" (Jer. 46:10)

24. "I will cause it to rain upon the earth _____ _____" (Gen. 7:4) (2 words)
25. Wings
26. "A time to _____, and a time to sew" (Eccles. 3:7)
27. Abbot, Fr.
28. Soft drink
30. Scrap of pottery
32. "Silly" birds
33. Greek letter
35. Calls to mind
38. Pathway
39. Rich cake

41. Actress Bancroft
43. Haughty conduct
44. Thought, Fr.
45. Milk provider
46. Biblical plain (Neh. 6:2)
47. Type of neckline
48. Golf peg

by Elaine Okupski

PUZZLE 24

ACROSS

1. "The gold of ____"
   (1 Chron. 29:4)
5. "Four men. . .____ in the. . .fire"
   (Dan. 3:25)
10. Sweaty class, abbr.
11. Shining circle indicating holiness
13. "What ye hear in the ____"
    (Matt. 10:27)
14. "He shewed himself alive after
    his ____" (Acts 1:3)
16. Period of time
17. Land where Cain lived after he
    killed Abel (Gen. 4:16)
18. South American language, abbr.
20. ____ sold his birthright
    (Heb. 12:16)
22. "I will ____ the loving-
    kindnesses of the Lord"
    (Isa. 63:7)
26. It is, contr.
28. Do again, prefix
29. Pimple
31. "____ by the Holy Ghost"
    (Rom. 15:16)
36. "To whom shall we ____?"
    (John 6:68)
37. Astronomical unit, abbr.
38. Adam and Eve's third son
    (Gen. 4:25)
40. "I. . .will ____ thee with my
    hand while I pass by"
    (Exod. 33:22)
44. Third Gospel, abbr.
45. "The ____ of the just is as the
    shining light" (Prov. 4:18)
47. Parentless child
48. Standard temperature and
    pressure, abbr.
49. Myself
50. "The ____ of all them that
    believe" (Rom. 4:11)

53. "It pleased the Lord to ____
    him" (Isa. 53:10)
56. Continent in the southern
    hemisphere, abbr.
57. Executive order, abbr.
59. Soviet Socialist Republic, abbr.
60. "Thy faithfulness shalt thou
    ____ in the very heavens"
    (Ps. 89:2)

DOWN

1. "____ not the widow, nor the
   fatherless" (Zech. 7:10)
2. Pod vegetable
3. Jesus Savior of Mankind, Lat.
   abbr.
4. "The ____ is over and gone"
   (Song of Sol. 2:11)
5. His name shall be called ____
   (Isa. 9:6)
6. "As ye have done it unto one of
   the ____ of these" (Matt. 25:40)
7. Cathode, Gk. abbr.
8. Anger
9. "The ____ tidings of the
   kingdom of God" (Luke 8:1)
12. Frame for weaving
15. "Stood a Lamb as it had been
    ____" (Rev. 5:6)
19. Preachy, Brit.
21. Universal time, coordinated,
    abbr.
23. Not elsewhere indicated, abbr.
24. Dorothy's imaginary land
25. "If a man walk in the ____, he
    stumbleth" (John 11:10)
27. Address abbreviation
30. Preposition
32. People who love and worship
33. Des Moines is the capital of this
    state, abbr.
34. Einsteinium, chem. symbol

35. "The _____ saith, It is not in me" (Job 28:14)
39. Adhesive strip
40. Used for grooming the hair
41. Replaces the president in case of sickness or death, abbr.
42. Questioning word
43. "In the third day he will _____ us up" (Hos. 6:2)
46. Greeting
48. Thrust a knife
51. A king (1 Kings 15:8)
52. Dweller, abbr.
54. Abram's birth place (Gen. 11:28)
55. Plural suffix
58. Exclamation

by Carole Stengel

PUZZLE 25

ACROSS

1. A Roman centurion (Acts 10:1)
7. The disciple that walked on water
11. We worship ____ God
12. Dutch, abbr.
13. Modern day Persia
15. "So that Christ's power may ____ on me" (2 Cor. 12:9)
17. "Mock him and spit on him, flog him and ____ him" (Mark 10:34)
19. Store
20. Maritime province, abbr.
21. Tint
23. Possessing height
25. Peter's original name
27. "Keep on praying for all the ____" (Eph. 6:18)
30. "I will send fire on ____" (Ezek. 39:6)
32. Neptunium, chem symbol
33. Laughter sound
34. Large green moth
36. Forward a letter
38. Preposition
39. Imaginary land where the Emerald City is
40. A synagogue ruler who was beaten (Acts 18:17)
42. A king of Judah (1 Kings 15:16)
44. Greek letter used for the ratio of a circle's circumference to its diameter
45. The disciple standing with Jesus' mother at the crucifixion (John 19:26)
46. He was called a Levi (Mark 2:14)
48. United Kingdom, abbr.
49. Indianapolis's state, abbr.
51. Worried expression (2 words)
53. Roman emperor who issued a decree for a census to be taken (Luke 2:1)
58. Each, abbr.
59. Letter that precedes em
61. Article that precedes a vowel
62. Northwestern state, abbr.
64. "God ____ His love among us" (1 John 4:9)
68. The brother of Jesus (Gal. 1:19)
70. Indefinite article
71. The peach state, abbr.
72. New Testament prophetess
74. "Asahel was as light of foot as a wild ____" (2 Sam. 2:18 KJV)
75. Relative by marriage
78. Distress signal
79. One of the twelve disciples (Matt. 10:3)

DOWN

1. Sore bumps on the toes
2. Runaway slave (Philem. 10)
3. Dweller, abbr.
4. Nickname for Edward
5. Paul's companion in Rome (2 Tim. 4:11)
6. Paul's companion during his second missionary journey (Acts 15:22, 40)
7. Jesus asked him, "Where shall we buy bread for these people?" (John 6:5)
8. Disciple from Lystra who traveled with Paul (Acts 16:1)
9. Period of time
10. "Lips that speak knowledge are a ____ jewel" (Prov. 20:15)
14. New covenant writings, abbr.
16. Doubted the resurrection (John 20:24–26)
18. Lieutenant, abbr.
22. Woman's name
24. Alights
26. Rich man from Arimathea (Matt. 27:57)
28. Salvation Army, abbr.
29. This man was raised from the dead
31. Magical inhabitant of a bottle
35. Norman's nickname
37. Northeastern area of the US, abbr.
38. Ruptured

39. Old style, abbr.
41. Coworker with Paul (2 Cor. 2:13)
42. One of the first disciples (John 1:35–42)
43. High priest during the time of Jesus (Matt. 26:3)
45. Christ's betrayer
47. Warrant officer, abbr.
50. Name unknown, abbr.
52. Male pronoun
54. If a man does this of the world, he forfeits his own soul (Matt. 16:26)
55. International peace-keeping organization, abbr.
56. Son of Nachor, father of Abraham (Luke 3:34 KJV)

57. "A longing fulfilled is _____ to the soul" (Prov. 13:19)
60. Lower limb
63. Preposition
65. Bright circle indicating saintliness
66. His sons were Shammai and Jada and his mother was Atarah (1 Chron. 2:26–28)
67. God created _____ and night
69. Morocco, abbr.
73. Negative
75. Input/output
76. National League, abbr.
77. Ourselves

NIV
by Michael J. Landi

PUZZLE 26

ACROSS

1. "The children of Gad called the altar ____" (Josh. 22:34)
3. "I have trusted also in the Lord; therefore I shall not ____" (Ps. 26:1)
7. A son of Zibeon (1 Chron. 1:40)
10. "The seed is ____ under their clods" (Joel 1:17)
12. "They ____ hands on them" (Acts 4:3)
14. "They are all ____ as an oven" (Hos. 7:7)
15. "Few there be that ____ it" (Matt. 7:14)
16. "Broughtest [Abram] forth out of ____ of the Chaldees" (Neh. 9:7)
17. "They left their father Zebedee in the ____" (Mark 1:20)
19. "Praise the Lord, all ye Gentiles; and ____ him" (Rom. 15:11)
20. "This man, after he had offered ____ sacrifice for sins for ever" (Heb. 10:12)
21. "I am as one mocked of ____ neighbour" (Job 12:4)
22. "The earth was without form, and ____" (Gen. 1:2)
23. "How ____ a man then understand?" (Prov. 20:24)
24. "He said, ____ is finished" (John 19:30)
25. Wail
26. "Turned from ____ eastward toward the sunrising" (Josh. 19:12)
28. "____, and all hills, fruitful trees, and all cedars" (Ps. 148:9)
30. "Round about the throne were four and twenty ____" (Rev. 4:4)
32. "____ it in a book" (Isa. 30:8)
33. "So ____, being many, are one body in Christ" (Rom. 12:5)
34. Metal
35. "In ____ and caves of the earth" (Heb. 11:38)
36. "When Jesus ____ finished these parables, he departed" (Matt. 13:53)

37. "Is ____ sick among you?" (James 5:14)
38. "I will put my hook in thy ____" (2 Kings 19:28)
39. "Let me ____ through thy land" (Deut. 2:27)
40. "Where ____ God my Maker?" (Job 35:10)
41. "The ____ are a people not strong" (Prov. 30:25)
42. "Rabbi, thou ____ the Son of God" (John 1:49)
43. "I saw, and behold a ____ in the midst of the earth" (Dan. 4:10)
44. Something that wipes away
47. "Sallu, ____, Hilkiah, Jedaiah" (Neh. 12:7)
48. "Thou shall not ____ to offer the first of thy ripe fruits" (Exod. 22:29)
49. Sodium, chem. symbol

DOWN

1. A son of Judah (1 Chron. 2:3)
2. "If thou ____ these things" (John 7:4)
3. "All iniquity shall ____ her mouth" (Ps. 107:42)
4. "And God said, ____ there be light" (Gen. 1:3)
5. "I shall never be ____ adversity" (Ps. 10:6)
6. "Achim begat ____" (Matt. 1:14)
7. Help
8. According to Freud, the selfish part of the self
9. "Turn aside, sit down ____" (Ruth 4:1)
11. "Lo ____, we have searched it" (Job 5:27)
13. "Rejoice ____ be glad in thee" (Ps. 70:4)
15. "I will send ____ into their hearts" (Neh. 12:9)
16. "Bakbukiah and ____, their brethren" (Neh. 12:9)
17. Recoils
18. "The archers ____ him" (1 Sam. 31:3)

19. "The ___ which is lent to the Lord" (1 Sam. 2:20)
20. "Wherein shall go no galley with ___" (Isa. 33:21)
22. You, Fr.
23. "The sweet ___ from a far country" (Jer. 6:20)
25. "Why beholdest thou the ___ that is in thy brother's eye?" (Luke 6:41)
26. Takes a chair
27. "To every man according to his ___" (Rom. 2:6)
28. Joseph's wife
29. Perfect excellence
31. Long periods of time
33. "The Lord ___ not in the wind" (1 Kings 19:11)
35. "She ___ on her lovers" (Ezek. 23:5)

36. Head coverings
37. "The children of Benjamin. . . dwelt at Michmash and ___" (Neh. 11:31)
38. Compass point
39. "___ for the peace of Jerusalem" (Ps. 122:6)
41. "The ___ of the covenant" (Heb. 9:4)
42. "The sons of Jether, Jephunneh, and Pispah, and ___" (1 Chron. 7:38)
43. "I will be ___ him a Father" (Heb. 1:5)
44. Letter that precedes em
45. Letter that follows em
46. Egyptian sun god

by Evelyn M. Boyington

ACROSS

1. "____ the lilies" (Matt. 6:28)
8. Woody Guthrie's son
11. Ann, Russ.
12. Moses' brother
13. Indianapolis' state, abbr.
14. Roman Catholic, abbr.
15. "They ____ unto them" (Exod. 12:36)
17. Bean curd
19. Apiece
21. Sews quickly
23. Turns away from sin
25. House of Lords, abbr.
26. The writings that contain the new covenant, abbr.
28. "Hole of the ____" (Isa. 11:8)
29. Nickel, chem. symbol
30. High male voices
34. "Every ____ of doctrine" (Eph. 4:14)
36. "He took. . .the ____ out of the house" (2 Chron. 33:15)
37. Three, prefix
38. More, suffix
39. "Pure ____ of water of life" (Rev. 22:1)
41. Overeaters Anonymous, abbr.
42. New England state, Concord is the capital, abbr.
44. Evergreen
45. Perform
46. Caleb's brother (Josh. 15:17)
50. "He riseth. . .and took a ____" (John 13:4)
52. Grievance
54. Metal thread
55. "Get thee hence, ____" (Matt. 4:10)
56. The meal's last course

DOWN

1. Joseph's profession (Mark 6:3)
2. One time
3. The Empire State, abbr.
4. Girl's name, for short
5. Bilhah's son (Gen. 35:25)
6. "They work, and ____" (2 Thess. 3:12)
7. Railed transportation, abbr.
8. Small insects
9. Throw out the ____
10. Burden
16. Chinese ruler
18. Son of Shemaiah (1 Chron. 26:7)
20. Rural route, abbr.
21. Noblemen, below a baron and above a knight, abbr.
22. Snake
24. Not applicable, abbr.
27. Tellurium, chem. symbol
31. Modern Bible translation, abbr.
32. Poem
33. Sea level, abbr.
34. "____ of heaven" (Mal. 3:10)
35. Small drip
37. Black sticky substance
40. Within, prefix
41. "Cake of ____ bread" (Exod. 29:23)
43. Howard, for short
44. Womanly, abbr.
46. Officers of the Guard, abbr.
47. Head covering
48. National Vision Associates, abbr.
49. Man's name
51. To make a mistake
53. Born, Fr.

PUZZLE 28

ACROSS

1. Fellow
5. Halfway, prefix
8. Charles, for short
12. Aircraft, prefix
13. Summer, Fr.
14. Alley Oop's girlfriend
15. "And he beat down the tower of Penuel, and ____ the men of the city" (Judg. 8:17)
16. Resident, abbr.
17. "Shall ____ words have an end?" (Job 16:3)
18. "We are troubled on every ____ ... we are ____" (2 Cor. 4:8) (2 words)
21. To make free of
22. Boy's name
23. "The ____ and flags shall wither" (Isa. 19:6)
26. Belonging to the author of much of the New Testament (2 words)
30. Referring to the nose, prefix
31. "Let me ____ the death of the righteous" (Num. 23:10)
32. Belonging to the National Security Agency, abbr.
33. Stutter
35. Sticks with a knife
36. Adjective suffix
37. Weep
38. "That the ____ ____ might through the thanksgiving of many redound to the glory of God" (2 Cor. 4:15)
45. Elbow-shaped pasta, for short
46. "But let your communication be, ____" (Matt. 5:37)
47. "____ that great city, that was clothed in fine linen" (Rev. 18:16)
48. ____ Domini

49. "Of ____, the family of the Erites" (Num. 26:16)
50. "But this woman since the time I came in hath not ceased to ____ my feet" (Luke 7:45)
51. Chinese food
52. Noise
53. Feminine name ending

DOWN

1. One of the Mamas and the Papas
2. Sun, prefix
3. "They bring thee ____ ____ heifer without spot" (Num. 19:2) (2 words)
4. "Far above all principality, and ____, and might, and ____" (Eph. 1:21) (2 words)
5. "The sons of Ezra were, Jether, and ____" (1 Chron. 4:17)
6. Roman road
7. "Hath done ____ unto the Spirit of grace" (Heb. 10:29)
8. "My ____ they ____, although I was an husband unto them" (Jer. 31:32)
9. Deception
10. "A strong delusion, that they should believe ____ ____" (2 Thess. 2:11)
11. "Though the number of the children of Israel be as the ____ of the sea" (Rom. 9:27)
19. Greek letters used for the ratio of a circle's circumference to its diameter
20. What you lose when you stand
23. Drs.' assistants
24. "Therefore, the children of Israel ____ not of the sinew which shrank" (Gen. 32:32)
25. That, Sp.

26. "And he answered. . .I go, _____: and went not" (Matt. 21:30)
27. Abbreviation for America
28. Where scientists work
29. Selective Service System, abbr.
31. "I made haste, and _____ not to keep thy commandments" (Ps. 119:60)
34. "I said of laughter, it is _____" (Eccles. 2:2)
35. Soak
37. "I will _____ all my raiment" (Isa. 63:3)
38. "Balak the king of Moab hath brought me from _____" (Num. 23:7)

39. "Thou hast smitten all mine enemies upon the cheek _____" (Ps. 3:7)
40. "Bakbukiah and _____ . . .were over against them in the watches" (Neh. 12:9)
41. "Salathiel, which was the son of _____" (Luke 3:27)
42. Got down from
43. "Have ye not _____ out the priests of the Lord" (2 Chron. 13:9)
44. To be, Lat.

by Janet W. Adkins

PUZZLE 29

ACROSS

1. Lot was told to go to the ____ (Gen. 19:17)
7. "There was no harm in the ____" (2 Kings 4:41)
9. Yes, Sp.
10. How many daughters Lot had (Gen. 19:8)
11. Who came to Lot (Gen. 19:1)
14. "He. . .did ____ unleavened bread" (Gen. 19:3)
16. "Bring them out ____ the place" (Gen. 19:12)
17. Dessert
18. Informed on a person
21. "The Lord ____ upon Sodom and upon Gomorrah" (Gen. 19:24)
24. "This ____ fellow came in to sojourn" (Gen. 19:9)
25. Abraham's nephew (Gen. 12:5)
27. Pittsburg's state, abbr.
28. In the year of our Lord, Lat. abbr.
29. One of the cities destroyed by God (Gen. 19:24)
32. Large vase
33. Farrow's first name
34. "Is there any taste in the white of an ____?" (Job 6:6)
35. "I cannot escape to the mountain, lest. . .I ____" (Gen. 19:19)
37. Held up Moses' hands (Exod. 17:12)
39. Lot was told to ____ (Gen. 19:17)
41. "Lot ____ out at the door" (Gen. 19:6)
43. Continent in the northern hemisphere, abbr.
44. Masculine pronoun
45. Corrida cheer
46. "Then said I, ____, I come" (Ps. 40:7)
48. "Their sin ____ very grievous" (Gen. 18:20)
50. "Now, this ____ is near" (Gen. 19:20)
51. "He overthrew ____ cities" (Gen. 19:25)

DOWN

1. They compassed Lot's house (Gen. 19:4)
2. "Neither shall ye ____ enchanment" (Lev. 19:26)
3. Nothing
4. "There came two angels to Sodom ____ even" (Gen. 19:1)
5. ____ Jima
6. "____ man hath seen God" (John 1:18)
7. "God destroyed the cities of the ____" (Gen. 19:29)
8. Golf peg
11. "They. . .brought them forth ____" (Gen. 19:17)
12. "Lot sat in the ____ of Sodom" (Gen. 19:1)
13. Another city destroyed by God
14. Bits per inch, abbr.
15. "They shall ____ the way of the Lord" (Gen. 18:19)
19. "Lot went out. . .____ shut the door" (Gen. 19:6)
20. Bashemath was her daughter (Gen. 26:34)
22. "God remembered ____" (Gen. 19:29)
23. They escaped with Lot (Gen. 19:16)
26. Thomas, for short
29. "He pressed upon them ____" (Gen. 19:3)

30. Japanese unit of distance
31. "Take. . .thy daughters, which are ____" (Gen. 19:15)
32. Unemployment insurance, abbr.
35. Female deer
36. Male adults
38. "Lot. . .rose ____ to meet them" (Gen. 19:1)
40. "She became a pillar of ____" (Gen. 19:26)
41. A woman in the army, abbr.
42. "I will ____ overthrow this city" (Gen. 19:21)
47. "____, let me escape" (Gen. 19:20)
48. Island, abbr.

49. Southeast, abbr.

by Elizabeth B. Smith

ACROSS

1. "They had ordained them elders in every ____" (Acts 14:23)
6. "Better is a dry ____, and quietness therewith, than an house full of sacrifices with strife" (Prov. 17:1)
11. "It is a ____ thing that the king requireth" (Dan. 2:11)
12. North central state whose capital is Madison, abbr.
13. J, K, L, __, __, __
14. American traitor, Benedict ____
15. Strange
16. South American language, abbr.
17. Do, ____, mi
18. Carpet
19. Hawaiian standard time, abbr.
20. "____ out heaven with the span" (Isa. 40:12)
22. "How long. . .____ thou be quiet?" (Jer. 47:6)
23. Assigned a monetary punishment
26. "They make a noise like a ____" (Ps. 59:6)
27. Curt
30. Do over, prefix
32. "Jesus, when he had cried again with a loud voice, yielded up the ____" (Matt. 27:50)
35. Exist
36. Adam's wife
38. "To him that overcometh will I give to eat of the ____ of life" (Rev. 2:7)
39. To arrange or plan
40. Help
41. This man had 454 descendents who escaped captivity in Babylon (Ezra 2:15)
44. Tender loving care, abbr.

45. "Wherefore come out from among them, and be ye ____" (2 Cor. 6:17)
46. Note of debt
48. Son of Judah (Gen. 38:4)
49. "And David was the ____ [son of Jesse]" (1 Sam. 17:14)
50. Degrees, suffix

DOWN

1. Smash
2. "____ and psalteries for singers" (2 Chron. 9:11)
3. Vase
4. Unidentified virus, prefix
5. "None of these things are ____ from him" (Acts 26:26)
6. Megawatts, abbr.
7. Kind of bread that Moses put in Aaron's hands for a wave offering to the Lord (Lev. 8:26–27)
8. Campfire treat made from graham cracker, marshmallow, and chocolate
9. Lasts
10. "We have both straw and provender enough, and room to ____ in" (Gen. 24:25)
17. "Though [your sins] be ____ like crimson, they shall be as wool" (Isa. 1:18)
20. "According to the working of his ____ power" (Eph. 1:19)
21. Nervous
23. Haze
24. What a spider spins
25. "I rejoiced ____" (3 John 3)
28. "A ____ shall be saved" (Rom. 9:27)
29. "The brightness of his glory, and the ____ image of his person" (Heb. 1:3)

31. "The tree of knowledge of good and ____" (Gen. 2:9)
33. Either
34. Kettle
37. European Defense Community, abbr.
42. "Sons of ____" (Gen. 46:23)
43. Modern Persia
45. "If any man will____ thee at the law, and take away thy coat, let him have thy cloke also" (Matt. 5:40)
46. The opposite of out
47. King of Bashan (Josh. 13:12)

by Cheryl Keiser

PUZZLE 31

ACROSS

1. Thrives
8. Boy's name, var. form
11. Played again
12. Set in
14. Two, Rom. num.
15. God told Moses His name was I ____
16. Overdose, abbr.
17. Milligram, abbr.
18. "Destroy. . .the ____" (Deut. 20:17)
20. Carrot family herb
23. Public transportation
24. Number of lepers that Christ healed
25. Charged particle
27. Christ is the Alpha and ____
29. And, Lat.
30. By the grace of God, Lat. abbr.
31. Preposition
32. Pull
33. Long walk
36. Tin container
37. Mr., Sp. abbr.
39. "The Lord will not ____ his people" (1 Sam. 12:22)
41. The self, according to Freud
43. "____, every one that thirsteth" (Isa. 55:1)
45. Possessive male pronoun
47. Preposition
48. Aaron's son (Exod. 6:25)
51. Childrens Bible club
53. Potato state
54. "____ my steps in thy word" (Ps. 119:133)
56. Russian ruler
57. "Take up thy ____, and go" (Matt. 9:6)
58. Church education, abbr.

DOWN

1. Monkey, for example
2. "Thy God ____!" (Isa. 52:7)
3. Either
4. Bags
5. IOU, in other words, abbr.
6. City in Zebulun (1 Chron. 6:77)
7. Tin, chemical symbol
8. Middle
9. Preposition
10. Feline's foot (2 words)
13. Paris university
15. Support organization for addicts, abbr.
19. African fly that spreads disease
21. Not out
22. Sea duck with soft feathers
26. King of Bashan (1 Kings 4:19)
28. Mythological snake-haired woman
31. "Howl, O ye ____ of Bashan" (Zech. 11:2)
34. "____ it be thou, bid me come" (Matt. 14:28)
35. Belonging to the leader of a rebellion against Moses (Num. 16)
36. Egyptian city
38. Arab chief
40. Feminine pronoun
42. Belonging to one of the sons of Judah (Num. 26:19)
44. "The dragon, that ____ serpent" (Rev. 20:2)
46. Filled with wonder
49. "Let us ____, and be merry" (Luke 15:23)
50. Animals, scientific suffix
51. Lemon beverage
52. Clinton's state, abbr.
55. Rubidium, chem. symbol

ACROSS

1. Son of Abijam (1 Kings 15:8)
4. Pull against the bit
8. Capable
12. Scottish cap
13. Jacob's brother
14. Narrow strip of wood
15. Representative
17. "If they drink any deadly thing, it shall not ____ them" (Mark 16:18)
18. "Yea, the sparrow hath found an house, and the swallow a ____" (Ps. 84:3)
19. Large water birds
20. "Stand ____ ____, and sin not" (Ps. 4:4) (2 words)
22. Unit of hay or cotton
24. Fathers
25. Son of Asa (Matt. 1:8)
29. "Neither do men light a candle, and put it under a bushel, but ____ ____ candlestick" (Matt. 5:15) (2 words)
30. Challenged
31. Period of time
32. "The ____ is worthy of his hire" (Luke 10:7)
34. Irish girl's name
35. Thomas Hardy heroine
36. "And if someone wants to sue you and take away your tunic, let him have your ____ as well" (Matt. 5:40 NIV)
37. "And four wagons and ____ oxen he gave unto the sons of Merari" (Num. 7:8)
40. Slipped
41. Pommel
42. Old Testament book named for the Jewish leader who supervised the rebuilding of Jerusalem's wall

46. "The children of ____ of Hezekiah, ninety and eight" (Neh. 7:21)
47. Region
48. Strong brew
49. Announces
50. "Wisdom hath builded her house, she hath ____ out her seven pillars" (Prov. 9:1)
51. Title of respect

DOWN

1. "I ____ no pleasant bread" (Dan. 10:3)
2. Texas hero, ____ Houston
3. Son of Aram (Matt. 1:4)
4. Son of Obed (Matt. 1:5)
5. "And ____ ____ astonied until the evening sacrifice" (Ezra 9:4) (2 words)
6. "Let them shut the doors, and ____ them" (Neh. 7:3)
7. Purchase
8. "As ____ ____ before her shearers is dumb" (Isa. 53:7) (2 words)
9. "And thou shalt make a veil of ____, and purple, and scarlet" (Exod. 26:31)
10. Swedish man's name
11. Diminutive suffix
16. Stitches
19. "I was ____ when they said unto me, Let us go into the house of the Lord" (Ps. 122:1)
20. False god
21. Grandmother
22. Drills
23. Anna's tribe (Luke 2:36)
25. Containers
26. Herod's wife (Mark 6:19)
27. Operatic solo
28. Armored vehicle

30. Song for two voices
33. "If ____ be partakers of this power over you, are not we rather?" (1 Cor. 9:12)
34. "And they came to ____, where were twelve wells of water" (Exod. 15:27)
36. "Create in me a ____ heart, O God" (Ps. 51:10)
37. Greek letters
38. An infinitesimal amount, a jot
39. "The beauty of old men is the ____ head" (Prov. 20:29)
40. "I will ____ thee the bride" (Rev. 21:9)

42. Nope
43. Before
44. Boxer Mohammed ____
45. "Go to the ant, thou sluggard; consider ____ ways" (Prov. 6:6)

by Elaine Okupski

PUZZLE 33

ACROSS

1. "He that loveth his ____ abideth in the light" (1 John 2:10)
6. "They. . .spake ____ one to another" (Mal. 3:16)
10. Anger
12. When you'll get to your destination, more or less, abbr.
13. "The ____ of the Lord. . .run to and fro" (Zech. 4:10)
16. "Let ____ the rich man glory in his riches" (Jer. 9:23)
17. Classifies
18. "We are the people of his pasture, and the sheep of his ____" (Ps. 95:7)
20. Dormitory helper, abbr.
21. "____ is the fulfilling of the law" (Rom. 13:10)
22. "Love worketh ____ ill to his neighbour" (Rom. 13:10)
23. Plural suffix
25. Month, abbr.
26. "Good ____ from a far country" (Prov. 25:25)
28. Article that precedes a vowel
29. "Jesus saith unto them, Come and ____" (John 21:12)
31. "Do not your ____ before men" (Matt. 6:1)
32. "The first covenant had. . .a worldly ____" (Heb. 9:1)
38. "For the wrath is come upon them to the ____"(1 Thess. 2:16)
41. Swine
42. Preposition
43. Noah's vessel
44. Assist
46. "He hath a great ____ for you" (Col. 4:13)
47. Nathan, for short
49. Tell an untruth

51. "The light of the body is the ____" (Luke 11:34)
53. And, Lat.
54. "A woman hath a familiar spirit at ____" (1 Sam. 28:7)
55. Extraterrestrial, abbr.

DOWN

1. "____ are the meek" (Matt. 5:5)
2. "By so much was Jesus made a surety of a better ____" (Heb. 7:22)
3. Head nurse, abbr.
4. Make a mistake
5. Radium, chem. symbol
6. Old English, abbr.
7. Number of commandments God gave to Moses
8. European Theater of Operations, abbr.
9. "The Lord is high above all ____" (Ps. 113:4)
11. "O ____, where is thy victory?" (1 Cor. 15:55)
14. Year old, abbr.
15. "Do not ____, my beloved brethren" (James 1:16)
18. "____ thy father and thy mother" (Exod. 20:12)
19. "A ____ commandment I give unto you" (John 13:34)
22. "Father, glorify thy ____" (John 12:28)
24. Sister, abbr.
27. Simon ____
30. Nothing
33. New England state, abbr.
34. "Ye are the ____ of the living God" (2 Cor. 6:16)
35. "They were all ____ at the mighty power of God" (Luke 9:43)

36. "I am the _____ of Sharon"
(Song of Sol. 2:1)
37. Backbone
39. "We spend our years as a _____
that is told" (Ps. 90:9)
40. Trapshooting
45. Narrow fish
48. A unit of value in Laos
50. Not out
52. "_____ shall be as gods"
(Gen. 3:5)

by Carole Stengel

PUZZLE 34

ACROSS

1. First book of the Bible
5. Jesus sat silent before this man (Matt. 27:11–14)
11. Cuckoo
12. David wrote most of this book, abbr.
14. "Everyone will be salted with ____" (Mark 9:49)
15. Appliance and electronics company, abbr.
16. Old Testament prophet
19. "Whoever loses his life for me will ____ it" (Matt. 16:25)
21. "Thou anointest my head with ____" (Ps. 23:5 KJV)
22. Name unknown, abbr.
23. He accused Paul of being out of his mind (Acts 26:24–25)
25. In the year of our Lord, Lat. abbr.
26. Letter's afterword
28. "He maketh me to ____ down in green pastures" (Ps. 23:2 KJV)
30. "____ is light" (1 John 1:5)
32. He was stoned to death after preaching to the Sanhedrin (Acts 7:59)
33. Beg
35. Printer's measure
36. Preposition
38. Greek for "my master" (Matt. 23:7)
41. "____ whatever gift he has received to serve others" (1 Pet. 4:10)
42. ____, so, la, ti, do
43. College English Association, abbr.
44. This beast spoke in a man's voice (2 Pet. 2:16 KJV)
46. Part of the high priest's breastplate (Exod. 28:30)
48. Exclamation
49. Ruthenium, chem. symbol
50. Leafy dish
51. Also known as Barsabbas (Acts 1:23)
53. The swallow had one for herself (Ps. 84:3)
56. Truckload, abbr.

58. Strategic Defense Initiative, abbr.
59. When Paul left Greece heading for Syria by way of Macedonia, he was accompanied by this Ephesian Christian (Acts 21:29)
62. Master of Arts in Teaching, abbr.
64. Undergraduate degree, abbr.
66. The man whose face was on the denarius (Matt. 22:20–21)
68. "For though I am ____ from you in body" (Col. 2:5)
71. Body of water
73. Born to Adam and Eve after the death of Abel (Gen. 4:25)
75. Visualize
78. America's abbreviation
79. A messenger of the church and companion of Paul (Phil. 2:25)

DOWN

1. One of the chief Philistine cities (Josh. 15:47)
2. Compass points
3. Secret disciple (John 3:1)
4. Twirl
6. "____ any of you lacks wisdom, he should ask God" (James 1:5)
7. "I will give you the crown of ____" (Rev. 2:10)
8. Seized by the crowd at Ephesus (Acts 19:29)
9. "I think it is right to refresh your memory as long as I live in the ____ of this body" (2 Pet. 1:13)
10. An Israelite
13. This man spoke slander about the Lord's disciples (Acts 9:1)
17. Brief greeting
18. Father of James (Matt. 10:3)
20. "____ down deep and laid the foundation of rock" (Luke 6:48)
23. Paul had a trial before him (Acts 24:1–4)
24. Fa, ____, la, ti, do
25. Consumed
27. Placed
29. Innings pitched, abbr.
31. "Isn't this the cup my master ____ from and also uses for divination?" (Gen. 44:5)

34. Dictionary of American English, abbr.
37. Paul was trained under him (Acts 22:3)
39. A blind beggar (Mark 10:46)
40. Companion of Paul who sold his property and gave to the apostles (Acts 4:36–37)
42. Dirt
45. Susan, for short
47. Egyptian sun god
48. Breakfast beverage, for short
52. Northwest state whose capital is Pierre
54. Address abbreviation
55. "I am the _____ vine, and my Father is the gardener" (John 15:1)
57. "Made him to _____ honey out of the rock" (Deut. 32:13 KJV)

60. "If a blind man leads a blind man, both will fall into a _____" (Matt. 15:14)
61. Self-addressed envelope, abbr.
63. _____ and crafts
65. Mr. Lincoln
67. Social Security, abbr.
69. "You shall _____ greater things than that" (John 1:50)
70. Gun organization, abbr.
72. Shakespeare's Much _____ About Nothing
74. He saw Noah's nakedness (Gen. 9:20–27)
76. Fifth day of the week, abbr.
77. Nebo, for example, abbr.

(NIV)
by Michael J. Landi

PUZZLE 35

ACROSS

1. But are ____ of your joy (1 Cor. 1:24)
5. "Now I have prepared. . .for the house of my God. . .all manner of precious stones, and ____ stones in abundance" (1 Chron. 29:2)
10. Each, abbr.
11. "I entreat thee also, true ____ fellow, help those women" (Phil. 4:3)
14. Federal Aviation Agency, abbr.
15. "This ____ said, I am able" (Matt. 26:61)
17. Laughter sound
18. "A meat offering baken in a ____" (Lev. 2:5)
20. Unit of verse measurement
22. District of Colombia, abbr.
23. Letter after em
24. Timothy, for short
25. Hare
27. Railway, abbr.
28. Do, ____, mi
29. Kilogram, abbr.
30. "This ____ the day which the Lord hath made" (Ps. 118:24)
31. "All things ____ together for good to them that love God" (Rom. 8:28)
32. The self, according to Freud
34. Common Era, abbr.
36. Louise, for short
37. Matured
38. Springfield's state, abbr.
39. "A time to weep, and a time to ____" (Eccles. 3:4)
41. Pierre's state
42. Paid, abbr.
43. Capital of Tibet

46. "I, John. . .was in the ____ that is called Patmos" (Rev. 1:9)
48. "As many as they found, both ____ and good" (Matt. 22:10)
50. "My fellow ____ in Christ Jesus" (Philem. 23)
52. "Thou shalt not muzzle the ____ when he treadeth out the corn" (Deut. 25:4)
53. Gym class, abbr.
55. Iridium, chem. symbol
56. To-do
57. Joined himself to a ____ of that country (Luke 15:15)

DOWN

1. People who give aid
2. 10 across
3. A type of grain
4. "Send to you Epaphroditus, my brother. . .and fellow ____" (Phil. 2:25)
6. Air Force, abbr.
7. "Joshua saved ____ the harlot alive" (Josh. 6:25)
8. Sheep's sound
9. Command
12. Kiloliter, abbr.
13. End of month, abbr.
15. Footnote, abbr.
16. "These only are my fellow ____ unto the kingdom of God" (Col. 4:11)
19. "Lest at ____ time thou dash thy foot against a stone" (Matt. 4:6)
21. Tattered
22. "And the ____ were called Christians first in Antioch" (Acts 11:26)
24. "Emptied her pitcher into the ____" (Gen. 24:20)

26. Two, prefix
31. "They _____ have repented long ago" (Matt. 11:21)
33. Exclamation of pain
35. "The four and twenty _____ . . . fell down and worshiped God" (Rev. 19:4)
36. Californian city, abbr.
39. Work
40. Sound of laughter
44. South America's language, abbr.
45. Western state, abbr.
46. Independent Order of Foresters, abbr.

47. A blunt nose
49. "Now also the _____ is laid unto the root of the trees (Matt. 3:10)
51. Anger
53. Greek letter used for the ratio of a circle's circumference to its diameter
54. And, Lat.

PUZZLE 36

ACROSS

1. "With the _____ angels" (Mark 8:38)
3. "The Holy _____ shall teach you" (Luke 12:12)
7. "They went. . .from _____. . .into Canaan" (Gen. 11:31)
8. A short laugh
9. Moses and _____ went before Pharaoh (Exod. 5:1)
10. "_____ is the way, which leadeth unto life" (Matt. 7:14)
12. Des Moines' state, abbr.
14. One of the twelve tribes (Num. 1:38)
15. David reigned there (2 Sam. 2:1)
16. Substantive, abbr.
18. "The _____ of thy life shall be many" (Prov. 4:10)
20. Northeastern area of the U.S., abbr.
21. Earned runs, abbr.
23. "Mine _____ is as nothing before thee" (Ps. 39:5)
24. "Our _____ is grown up" (Ezra 9:6)
29. Graduate degree, abbr.
31. A poem
32. Some were clay and some iron (Dan. 2:42)
34. "These are the _____ covenants" (Gal. 4:24)
36. "Being reviled, _____ bless" (1 Cor. 4:12)
38. "God saw that _____ was good" (Gen. 1:10)
39. An unclean thing (Lev. 11:29)
41. Santa Fe's state, abbr.
42. A city belonging to the tribe of Naphtali (Josh. 19:38–39)
44. A mongrel

47. "By faith they passed through the _____ sea" (Heb. 11:29)
49. Warrant officer, abbr.
50. News agency, abbr.

DOWN

1. "With his _____ spread up to heaven" (1 Kings 8:54)
2. "Confess that Jesus Christ is _____" (Phil. 2:11)
3. Guaranteed annual wage, abbr.
4. "Perform unto the Lord thine _____" (Matt. 5:33)
5. Salvation Army, abbr.
6. "Deliver me out of all _____" (1 Sam. 26:24)
7. The joining of two or more things into one
8. "Provide things _____ in the sight of all men" (Rom. 12:17)
11. Man's name, for short
13. Over again
17. "Abraham _____ Isaac" (Gen. 25:19)
19. "A bruised _____ shall he not break" (Matt. 12:20)
22. Do, _____, mi
23. I _____. God's name given to Moses
25. "I am the _____ and the offspring of David" (Rev. 22:16)
26. "He revealeth his _____ unto his servants" (Amos 3:7)
27. "_____ I opened my mouth" (Ezek. 3:2)
28. Stitches
30. "One _____ or one tittle shall in no wise pass from the law" (Matt. 5:18)

33. "When we shall _____ him" (Isa. 53:2)
35. "If any _____ have children" (1 Tim. 5:4)
37. "The noise of a _____, and the noise of the rattling of the wheels" (Nah. 3:2)
40. Zaccur's father (Neh. 3:2)
43. "To be sin for us, who knew _____ sin" (2 Cor. 5:21)
44. Pa's wife
45. "He was taken _____; and a cloud received him out of their sight" (Acts 1:9)
46. "Given _____ hospitality" (Rom. 12:13)
48. "Without me ye can _____ nothing" (John 15:5)

by Carole Stengel

PUZZLE 37

ACROSS

1. Formal request for one's presence
9. Preposition
11. Sodium, chem. symbol
12. Nickel, chem. symbol
13. Man's name
14. "____ it with thy might" (Eccles. 9:10)
15. "The Lord knoweth the ____ of the wise" (1 Cor. 3:20)
18. "____ hath he quickened" (Eph. 2:1)
19. Worries
20. Belonging to
22. Nurse, abbr.
23. Belonging to Judah's firstborn (Num. 26:19)
24. The Anointed One
26. Frigid
29. Indefinite article
30. Flightless bird
32. "For God ____ loved the world" (John 3:16)
33. Concept
36. Twelfth-grader, abbr.
37. Frightened
39. Article that precedes a vowel
40. "Phebe our ____" (Rom. 16:1)
43. Anger
44. Floss
47. "That have the rule ____ you" (Heb. 13:17)
50. Atomic energy, abbr.
52. Not, prefix
53. "Ye might have life through his ____" (John 20:31)
54. Shut noisily
55. Bristle
56. "Is my hand shortened at all, that it cannot ____?" (Isa. 50:2)
57. Light wood

DOWN

1. "Who also maketh ____ for us" (Rom. 8:34)
2. Slang negative
3. Accustomed to something unpleasant
4. Big cat
5. Small children
6. "Groweth of ____ own" (Lev. 25:5)
7. Writings that Jews and Christians have in common, abbr.
8. "I will fear ____ evil" (Ps. 23:4)
9. Smells
10. Spring of water
16. Preposition
17. Altitudes, abbr.
20. Exclamation
21. Scared, for short
24. Group of singers
25. India, abbr.
27. Son of Becher (1 Chron. 7:8)
28. Lutetium, chem. symbol
31. Someone who takes advantage
32. Southern continent, abbr.
34. Apiece, abbr.
35. Feelers
38. Wrinkle
41. Exhausted
42. Trite
45. "A ____ without blemish" (1 Pet. 1:19)
46. Promises
48. Various, abbr.
49. Suffix
51. Shade tree

by Cheryl Keiser

1 2 3 4 5 6 7 8 9 10
11 12 13 14
15 16 17 18
19 20 21 22
23 24 25
26 27 28 29
30 31 32 33 34 35
36 37 38 39
40 41 42
43 44 45 46
47 48 49 50 51 52
53 54 55
56 57

PUZZLE 38

ACROSS

1. Division of opposing parties
5. "_____ thy way unto the Lord" (Ps. 37:5)
8. Exclamation
9. Small amount
10. "_____ my Father's house are many mansions" (John 14:2)
11. "Jesus saith unto them, Come and _____" (John 21:12)
12. Nativity set
15. Indianapolis's state, abbr.
16. Where Goliath was from (2 Sam. 21:22)
17. Social equal
19. Overdose, abbr.
20. New Testament book that follows Galatians, abbr.
21. Isaiah's father (Isa. 1:1)
23. Exclamation of satisfaction
25. Sound used to attract attention
27. Rachel's handmaid given to Jacob to bear a son (Gen. 30:3)
29. "_____ is a rewarder of them that diligently seek him" (Heb. 11:6)
30. "_____ ye therefore, and teach all nations" (Matt. 28:19)
31. Lower limb
33. Legendary bird of prey
36. Line, abbr.
37. Time past
38. Office of Technology Assessment
39. Cow's noise
40. Dover's state, abbr.
41. "Thy word have I _____ in mine heart" (Ps. 119:11)
43. "There shall in no wise enter into it any thing that defileth, neither whatsoever worketh _____" (Rev. 21:27)
47. "Why beholdest thou the _____ that is in thy brother's eye?" (Luke 6:41)
49. Where Job lived (Job 1:1)
50. High ranking Turkish official
51. "He planteth an _____, and the rain doth nourish it" (Isa. 44:14)
52. Man who died after he had deceived the apostles (Acts 5:1–5)

DOWN

1. Father of Israelite spy (Num. 13:10)
2. Lower part of the face
3. Yes, Sp.
4. Land that lies ten miles east of Beer-sheba (Neh. 11:26)
5. Hidden store
6. The Philistines put five golden _____ in the Ark of the Covenant as a trepass offering when they returned it (1 Sam. 6:4)
7. To stick, adhere
13. Hebrew unit of measure (Exod. 16:36)
14. More, suffix
16. Leave
18. Steal
21. Solomon planted these trees in terraces up to the temple (2 Chron. 9:11)
22. City of David (2 Chron. 5:2)
24. Circle of light
26. Herod's wife and sister-in-law (Luke 3:19)
28. Not him
32. Elisha's servant (2 Kings 4:12)
34. Begins with Genesis and ends with Malachi, abbr.

35. Pertaining to the body
36. Unwilling
37. Arab country
40. "My meat is to ____ the will of him that sent me" (John 4:34)
42. Pronoun for a thing
44. "____ still, and know that I am God" (Ps. 46:10)
45. Joshua's father (Josh. 1:1)
46. King of Bashan (1 Kings 4:19)
47. Mother
48. Old style, abbr.

ACROSS

1. "____ and see" (John 1:39)
5. Town near Bethel (Josh. 7:2)
6. "Them that ____ in riches" (Mark 10:24)
11. Valley near Jerusalem (Josh. 15:8)
13. "____ is he" (Rom. 14:22)
14. Aluminum, chem. symbol
15. Nashville's state, abbr.
16. "I am the ____" (John 14:6)
18. "Trees of the Lord are full of ____" (Ps. 104:16)
19. Large stringed instruments
21. Do, ____, mi
22. "We beheld his ____" (John 1:14)
24. "Like a refiner's ____" (Mal. 3:2)
26. East Indies, abbr.
27. "Whoseover ____ in him should not perish" (John 3:16)
31. "A great ____ dragon" (Rev. 12:3)
33. "Unto the ____ of the earth" (Acts 13:47)
34. Resound
35. "The ____ of death is sin" (1 Cor. 15:56)
37. "To sit up ____" (Ps. 127:2)
38. "When ____ the king had heard these things, he was troubled" (Matt. 2:3)
40. "Naphtali is a ____ let loose" (Gen. 49:21)
43. Calendar numbers
46. Victory in Europe, abbr.
47. "He was ____ the world" (John 1:10)
49. Accomplish

52. "He ____, and denied not" (John 1:20)
56. "Made it a ____ of thieves" (Matt. 21:13)
57. "No man hath ____" (John 3:13)
58. Road, abbr.

DOWN

1. "Poured out the ____ money" (John 2:15)
2. "Took no ____ with them" (Matt. 25:3)
3. St. Paul's state, abbr.
4. "He cannot ____ into the kingdom of God" (John 3:5)
5. "I ____ the living bread" (John 6:51)
6. "Father, glorify ____ name" (John 12:28)
7. Egyptian sun god
8. ____ and downs
9. "He that ____ his rod" (Prov. 13:24)
10. Kind, variety
12. "Glory as of the ____ ____ of the Father"(John 1:14) (2 words)
16. "The ____ was made by him" (John 1:10)
17. "Love one another, ____ I have loved you" (John 15:12)
19. Company, abbr.
20. "Go thy way; thy son ____" (John 4:50)
23. "As much as ____ in you" (Rom. 12:18)
24. Iron, chem. symbol
25. "As many as ____ him, to them gave he power" (John 1:12)
28. Printer's measure

29. "I. . .was in the _____ that is called Patmos" (Rev. 1:9)
30. "_____ fast that which is good" (1 Thess. 5:21)
32. "Jesus Christ, Who _____ for us" (1 Thess. 5:9–10)
36. Gun lobbyists, abbr.
39. Eastern seaboard state, abbr.
41. "_____ man spake like this" (John 7:46)
42. Type style
44. Correspondence enclosure, abbr.
45. Doctorate degree, abbr.
48. Negative votes
50. Committee for Economic Development, abbr.
51. "To this _____ I was born" (John 18:37)
53. State where man first flew, abbr.
54. Far East, abbr.
55. Northwest state, abbr.

by Rebecca Souder

Puzzle 40

ACROSS

1. "Ye tithe ____ and rue and all manner of herbs" (Luke 11:42)
4. "But the ____ are beaten out with a staff" (Isa. 28:27)
9. Sound of hesitation
10. "I will sing of the mercies of the Lord for ____" (Ps. 89:1)
13. Poem
14. "Then took Mary a pound of ointment of ____" (John 12:3)
17. Royal Air Force, abbr.
18. African antelope
20. "All thy garments smell of myrrh, and ____" (Ps. 45:8)
22. "I will give unto thee the ____ of the kingdom of heaven" (Matt. 16:19)
23. "I. . .brought thee out of ____ of the Chaldees" (Gen. 15:7)
24. Republic of Rwanda, abbr.
25. "They slew the kings of Midian . . .namely, ____" (Num. 31:8)
27. Biblical plain (Neh. 6:2)
28. Arid
29. "Ye pay tithe of mint and ____ and cummin" (Matt. 23:23)
33. Follows em
34. A greeting
35. "Beaten out with a staff, and the ____ with a rod" (Isa. 28:27)
38. Sixteenth letter of the Hebrew alphabet
39. Myself
40. "Thou shouldest be for salvation unto the ____ of the earth" (Acts 13:47)
41. Sweet potatoes
43. "The smoke of the ____. . . ascended up before God" (Rev. 8:4)

45. Cereal grains
46. First day of the week, abbr.
47. Twice, prefix
49. City in Nevada
50. Native of Serbia
53. Canned meat product
54. "Such ____ as the queen of Sheba gave king Solomon" (2 Chron. 9:9)

DOWN

1. "Faith as a grain of ____ seed" (Matt. 17:20)
2. Mischievous child
3. Moslem monastery
4. "They presented unto him gifts; gold and ____" (Matt. 2:11)
5. "____ shalt thou be with me in paradise" (Luke 23:43)
6. Record's replacement, abbr.
7. Zeus's sister
8. "Thy plants are. . .spikenard and ____" (Song of Sol. 4:13–14)
11. Bible division within a chapter
12. Printer's measure
15. "His belly is as bright ____" (Song of Sol. 5:14)
16. Grain
19. Library science, abbr.
21. "The ____ is my shepherd" (Ps. 23:1)
23. Infinite
26. Southern state, abbr.
30. Iowa University, abbr.
31. Not large, abbr.
32. To correct
34. "They filled a sponge with vinegar, and put it upon ____" (John 19:29)
36. ____ and outs

37. "They presented unto him gifts; gold, and. . .____" (Matt. 2:11)
38. Prayer endings
39. Do, re, ____
42. Opposite of nay
44. Worthless dog
48. Frozen water
50. Samarium, chem. symbol
51. Undergraduate degree, abbr.
52. Seventh note of the musical scale

ACROSS

1. Religious leaders of Jesus' day (Matt. 23:2)
7. Jesus is called the ____ of man
10. Philadelphia's state, abbr.
11. Barnabas was this (Acts 4:36)
13. Heavy work shoe
15. Abigail, for short, alt. spelling
16. Girl, Scot.
17. Eclipse, abbr.
19. Interior, abbr.
20. Nahor's concubine (Gen. 22:24)
22. Belonging to America's spy agency, abbr.
24. National Guard, abbr.
26. Do, ____, mi
27. Doctor who delivers babies, abbr.
28. "The ____ are a people not strong" (Prov. 30:25)
29. "They. . .are choked with ____" (Luke 8:14)
30. French word used to identify a woman by her maiden name
31. Kid's candy
32. Ostrich like bird
35. Organ remover
38. "A ____ prepared for the Lord" (Luke 1:17)
42. Written composition
43. Put in writing, var. spelling
47. Jiphtah and ____ (Josh. 15:43)
49. Great arteries
50. "Which stilleth the noise of the ____" (Psalm 65:7)
51. Long, narrow fish

DOWN

1. Matthew the ____ (Matt. 10:3)
2. One who renounces his faith
3. "All our righteousnesses are as filthy ____" (Isa. 64:6)
4. "We had the ____ of death in ourselves" (2 Cor. 1:9)
5. "Rebuke not an ____" (1 Tim. 5:1)
6. Compass point
7. A brother or sister, for short
8. Off Track Betting, abbr.
9. "Love his ____ as himself" (Mark 12:33)
12. Regards as precious
14. Like a frog
18. Breakfast food
21. Account of, abbr.
23. Religious education, abbr.
25. Area of Israel that adjoins the Sinai Peninsula
32. And, Lat.
33. Pertaining to the mind
34. Extends across
36. Jesus is called the ____ of life (John 6:48)
37. French spelling of Andrew
38. Pod dwellers
39. To be, Lat.
40. Occupational Safety and Health Agency, abbr.
41. Linear Yard Area, abbr.
44. Negative
45. Resident or follower, suffix
46. Curved shape
48. Laughter sound

by Cheryl Keiser

PUZZLE 42

ACROSS

1. Person who makes perfume
8. "Ten women shall ____ your bread in one oven" (Lev. 26:26)
11. Any person
12. "The noise of the stamping of the ____ of his strong horses" (Jer. 47:3)
14. Inspector General, abbr.
15. Edible Japanese plant
16. Eggs
18. Near, abbr.
19. "No man putteth a piece of ____ cloth unto an old garment" (Matt. 9:16)
20. Temporary route
23. Teacher's helper, abbr.
24. Physician, abbr.
25. "Take thee a ____ razor, and cause it to pass upon thine head" (Ezek. 5:1)
26. Four, Rom. num.
27. South Vietnamese coin
28. Short for potassium nitrate, Br.
31. "He shall sit as a ____ and purifier of silver" (Mal. 3:3)
35. "There shall be weeping and ____ of teeth" (Matt. 8:12)
36. "This do ye; ____ your beasts, and go" (Gen. 45:17)
37. Island nation, abbr.
38. Too much of a drug, abbr.
40. Therefore
41. Putting threads together to make fabric
45. Impersonal pronoun
47. Current of warm water that affects the weather (2 words)
49. Paul's occupation
53. Peach state, abbr.
54. Dorcas's occupation (Acts 9:39)
55. "Come unto ____, all ye that labour" (Matt. 11:28)
56. "In the beginning ____ created the heaven and the earth" (Gen. 1:1)

DOWN

1. Coloring with a brush
2. "Grave upon it, like the ____s of a signet" (Exod. 28:36)
3. Track transportation, abbr.
4. Sinks below surface of water
5. "Is a candle brought to be put ____ a bushel?" (Mark 4:21)
6. Cat's cry
7. "Peter knocked. . .a damsel came to hearken, named ____" (Acts 12:13)
8. Noah's occupation (2 words)
9. Flying soldiers, abbr.
10. Dorothy's state, abbr.
13. "Shepherds. . .keeping watch ____ their flock by night" (Luke 2:8)
17. Tax enforcement organization, abbr.
21. Old English, abbr.
22. "Take I pray thee. . .And he ____ him, and he took it" (Gen. 33:11)
25. Overheat
29. Flaps
30. Extemely high frequency, abbr.
32. For example, Lat. abbr.
33. Northern continent, abbr.
34. "Though they be ____ like crimson, they shall be as wool" (Isa. 1:18)
38. Like a sheep
39. Glove

41. "We will eat our own bread, and
    ____ our own apparel" (Isa. 4:1)
42. Antlered animal
43. Musical term to indicate
    "animated," abbr.
44. "There was ____ room for them
    in the inn" (Luke 2:7)
46. Hot or cold beverage
48. A son of Zilpah (Gen. 35:26)
50. Nickel, chem. symbol
51. Total loss, abbr.
52. Southwestern state whose capital
    is Jefferson City, abbr.
53. "____ ye therefore, and teach all
    nations" (Matt. 28:19)

PUZZLE 43

ACROSS

1. "The ____ of God is eternal life" (Rom. 6:23)
4. "Without him was ____ any thing made" (John 1:3)
6. "That was the ____ light" (John 1:9)
9. "The ____ shineth in darkness" (John 1:5)
11. "Which were ____, not of blood" (John 1:13)
12. "Was made flesh and ____ among us" (John 1:14)
14. Precious stone
15. Dock warrant, abbr.
17. Chemical suffix
18. Young woman
20. Also
21. His Royal Highness, abbr.
22. "Smote the ____ into his temples" (Judg. 4:21)
24. Hebrew name for God, comb. form
25. "But as many as ____ him" (John 1:12)
28. The first man
31. Electron volt, abbr.
32. Four, Rom. num.
33. Belonging to a Canaanite god
37. "A ____ commandment I give unto you" (John 13:34)
39. "The ____ comprehended it not" (John 1:5)
42. Emergency Relief Organization, abbr.
43. To balk, Scot.
44. Office of Strategic Services, abbr.
47. Year, abbr.
48. "But was sent to ____ ____ of that Light" (John 1:8) (2 words)
51. Overseas News Service, abbr.
52. European Theater of Operations, abbr.
53. "Full of grace and ____" (John 1:14)
55. "I come baptizing with ____" (John 1:31)
56. Church, abbr.
57. Negative vote

DOWN

1. "The Word was ____" (John 1:1)
2. "The Word was made ____" (John 1:14)
3. "Take thee a ____" (Ezek. 4:1)
4. New England state, abbr.
5. A division of Scripture
6. Thomas, for short
7. Railroad, abbr.
8. "To ____ the heavy burdens" (Isa. 58:6)
10. Gross ton, abbr.
11. "Them that ____ on his name" (John 1:12)
13. "The ____ was made by him" (John 1:10)
14. "But ____ and truth came" (John 1:17)
16. "In the beginning was the ____" (John 1:1)
19. Suffix
21. "Two disciples ____ him speak" (John 1:37)
23. Fifty-one, Rom. num.
26. "I am the true ____" (John 15:1)
27. "Which lighteth ____ man" (John 1:9)
29. Side by side
30. "Builder and ____ is God" (Heb. 11:10)

34. "How ye ought to ____ every man" (Col. 4:6)
35. "And ____ ____ out to husband-men" (Mark 12:1) (2 words)
36. Church school, in other words, abbr.
38. "Thou art ____, O Lord" (Rev. 4:11)
40. Place for competition
41. "The only begotten ____" (John 1:18)
45. Son of Adam

46. Soviet Socialist Republic, abbr.
48. "Every knee should ____" (Phil. 2:10)
49. "He gave power ____ become" (John 1:12)
50. "Did shine as the ____" (Matt. 17:2)
54. Tantalum, chem. symbol

by Rebecca Souder

PUZZLE 44

ACROSS

1. Jesus is the good ____
8. Thank you, Br.
10. Jesus made water into this at Cana
11. Prophet in Jerusalem that warned Paul he would be arrested (Acts 21:10–11)
14. To set apart for a duty of the church
15. "For we wrestle not against flesh and blood. . .but. . .against the ____ of the darkness"(Eph. 6:12)
16. To have a strong smell
17. The people of Athens had an altar to an ____God(Acts 17:23)
19. This servant of God must be the husband of one wife, grave, and not double-tongued (1 Tim. 3:8–12)
20. "____, and ye shall receive" (John 16:24)
23. Tower where Jacob (Israel) camped on his way to Canaan (Gen. 35:21)
25. The opposite of live
27. Poisonous snakes (Deut. 32:33)
29. Myself
30. Where Israel was held in bondage for centuries until Moses led them to freedom
31. Remaining residue after something has been burned
33. Pertaining to farming, prefix
34. A servant of the high priest lost this momentarily to Peter's sword
36. God asks us to improve or ____ our ways (Jer. 7:3)
37. "Teaching them to ____ all things" (Matt. 28:20)
40. ____ and fro
41. Second note of the musical scale
42. People sacrificed this to atone for sin
45. Helped Moses speak before Pharaoh
48. Revise
50. One who held up Moses' hands at the battle of Amalek (Exod. 17:12)
51. "Let us draw near with a true heart in full ____ of faith" (Heb. 10:22)

DOWN

1. The Word of God is sharper than this
2. "The labourer is worthy of his ____" (Luke 10:7)
3. Terminated
4. Reached a maximum
5. "Thus saith the Lord unto the ____ that keep my sabbaths" (Isa. 56:4)
6. The absence of light
7. Ring of light
8. Spins
9. Balaam's spoke to him by God's power
12. Firearm
13. "____ of false prophets, which come to you in sheep's clothing" (Matt. 7:15)
18. Negative
21. "Seek ye first the ____ of God" (Matt. 6:33)
22. Swine
24. God's name for Himself: I ____ (Exod. 3:14)
25. The fourth of Israel's judges, a woman

26. Sight organs
27. Ancestor of family of porters who returned from exile (Neh. 7:45)
28. "Children, obey your _____ in the Lord" (Eph. 6:1)
32. "Is not my word like as a fire? saith the Lord; and like a _____ that breaketh the rock" (Jer. 23:29)
33. Sluggards should learn from this insect

35. Assyrian region from which Sargon brought men to populate devastated Samaria (2 Kings 17:24)
38. Boyfriend, Fr.
39. The conscious self
43. Woman's name
44. Linear, abbr.
46. Railed transportation, abbr.
47. Sodium, chem. symbol
49. Technetium, chem. symbol

PUZZLE 45

ACROSS

1. "Let the earth bring forth. . . ____, and creeping thing, and beast of the earth" (Gen. 1:24)
8. Southern continent, abbr.
10. Precipitates
11. "The earth was without ____" (Gen. 1:2)
13. Judah's son (Gen. 38:3)
14. When you're going to leave, more or less, abbr.
15. Anger
16. "____ there be light" (Gen. 1:3)
17. Christ's followers, abbr.
19. "God ____ the heaven" (Gen. 1:1)
21. Seventh note of the musical scale
22. "Divide the waters ____ the waters" (Gen. 1:6)
23. Ruthenium, chem. symbol
24. Fiddler crab genus
26. "Let the ____ under the heaven be gathered together" (Gen. 1:9)
29. War of the ____
31. "The evening and the ____ were the third day" (Gen. 1:13)
34. Extraterrestrial, abbr.
35. "Where ____ you?" (Gen. 3:9 NIV)
37. "Breathed ____ his nostrils the breath of life" (Gen. 2:7)
38. "In the ____ God" (Gen. 1:1)
41. "The waters called he ____" (Gen. 1:10)
42. Common preposition
43. "He did ____ it under his raiment" (Judg. 3:16)
45. "There shall come a ____ out of Jacob" (Num. 24:17)
47. Touchdown, abbr.

49. Negative
50. "Thou art an ____ man" (Luke 19:21)
53. "And ____ said, Let there be light" (Gen. 1:3)
55. Day when plants were created
56. "Hath God said, ____ shall not eat of every tree?" (Gen. 3:1)
57. Iron, chem. symbol

DOWN

1. "Every living ____ that moveth" (Gen. 1:21)
2. Support organization for alcoholics, abbr.
3. Binds
4. Explosive, abbr.
5. Illegal drug referred to as acid, abbr.
6. "According to the ____-knowledge of God" (1 Pet. 1:2)
7. God's name for Himself: I ____ (Exod. 3:14)
8. "Whose ____ is in itself" (Gen. 1:11)
9. "For dust thou ____" (Gen. 3:19)
11. "God called the ____ Heaven" (Gen. 1:8)
12. One who raises
16. French article
18. Decorative loop on ribbon
19. "The ____ and the bear shall feed" (Isa. 11:7)
20. "Neither shadow of ____" (James 1:17)
25. "Ye shall be ____ gods" (Gen. 3:5)
27. Preposition
28. "Declare his works with ____" (Ps. 107:22 ASV)
30. Droops

32. Part of Scripture that contains the new covenant, abbr.

33. "And God saw that it was ____" (Gen. 1:10)

36. Smallest state, abbr.

38. "God made the ____ of the earth" (Gen. 1:25)

39. "Let the ____ bring forth grass" (Gen. 1:11)

40. "Thou shalt ____ eat of it" (Gen. 2:17)

41. Man's name, for short

44. "Under the shadow of my ____" (Gen. 19:8)

45. "God ____ every thing that he had made" (Gen. 1:31)

46. "Fools, shall not ____ therein" (Isa. 35:8)

48. "On the seventh ____ God ended his work" (Gen. 2:2)

51. East Indies, abbr.

52. Education, abbr.

54. Eastern seacoast state, abbr.

by Rebecca Souder

PUZZLE 46

ACROSS

1. "Thou art an ____ people unto the Lord" (Deut. 7:6)
3. "The Holy ____ shall teach you" (Luke 12:12)
7. "They went. . .from ____. . .into Canaan" (Gen. 11:31)
8. A short laugh
9. Moses and ____ went before Pharaoh (Exod. 5:1)
10. "____ is the way, which leadeth unto life" (Matt. 7:14)
12. Three, prefix
13. Des Moines' state, abbr.
15. One of the twelve tribes (Num. 1:38)
16. David reigned there (2 Sam. 2:1)
17. Antimony, chem. symbol
19. Twelve months
21. Europium, chem. symbol
22. Northeastern region of the U.S., abbr.
23. Earned runs, abbr.
25. Sixth note of the musical scale
27. "The eyes of Israel were dim for ____" (Gen. 48:10)
28. "If thy brother ____ against thee, rebuke him" (Luke 17:3)
32. Pa's wife
34. Poem
35. Bonds
37. "____ of every sort shalt thou bring into the ark" (Gen. 6:19)
39. "Being reviled, ____ bless" (1 Cor. 4:12)
41. "God saw that ____ was good" (Gen. 1:10)
42. An unclean thing (Lev. 11:29)
45. Coal scuttle
47. Gym, in other words, abbr.
48. Colorado's neighbor, abbr.
49. "A land whose stones are ____" (Deut. 8:9)
51. Mongrel
53. "As ____ as blood" (2 Kings 3:22)
55. "My flesh is clothed with ____" (Job 7:5)
56. Sash worn with a kimona

DOWN

1. "With his ____ spread up to heaven" (1 Kings 8:54)
2. "Confess that Jesus Christ is ____" (Phil. 2:11)
3. Guaranteed annual wage, abbr.
4. "Let there be now an ____ betwixt us" (Gen. 26:28)
5. Asian garment, alt. spelling
6. "Deliver me out of all ____" (1 Sam. 26:24)
7. The joining of two or more things
8. "Whatsoever things are ____. . . think on these things" (Phil. 4:8)
11. Sunbeam
14. Over again
18. "Abraham ____ Isaac" (Gen. 25:19)
20. "A bruised ____ shall he not break" (Matt. 12:20)
24. Regarding, abbr.
26. Airspeed indicator, abbr.
27. God's name for Himself: I ____
29. "I am the ____ and the offspring of David" (Rev. 22:16)
30. "He revealeth his ____ unto his servants" (Amos 3:7)
31. Stitches
33. "One ____ or tittle shall in no wise pass from the law" (Matt. 5:18)

36. "When we shall _____ him"
    (Isa. 53:2)
38. "If any _____ have children. . . ,
    let them first learn to shew piety
    at home" (1 Tim. 5:4)
40. "The noise of a _____" (Nah. 3:2)
43. Great work
44. Zaccur's father (Neh. 3:2)
46. Either

50. "To be sin for us, who knew
    _____ sin" (2 Cor. 5:21)
51. 2000, Rom. num.
52. "Given _____ hospitality"
    (Rom. 12:13)
54. "Without me ye can _____
    nothing" (John 15:5)

PUZZLE 47

ACROSS

1. "The ____ of God is eternal life" (Rom. 6:23)
5. "Jesus Christ our ____" (Rom. 1:3)
9. Civil Servant, abbr.
11. "To God ____ wise, be glory" (Rom. 16:27)
12. "Walk in the ____, as he is" (1 John 1:7)
13. Of age, Lat. abbr.
14. "The fallow ____" (Deut. 14:5)
15. "The grace ____ our Lord Jesus Christ be with you all" (Rev. 22:21)
16. Tender loving care, abbr.
17. "Whom I ____ with my spirit in the gospel" (Rom. 1:9)
19. "The Word was made flesh, and ____ among us" (John 1:14)
21. New England state, abbr.
22. Electrical engineer, abbr.
23. Abraham's wife (Gen. 12:5)
24. Southern continent, abbr.
25. "We have seen his ____ in the east" (Matt. 2:2)
26. All news station, abbr.
27. "He ever ____ to make intercession" (Heb. 7:25)
31. Heligram, abbr.
32. Got down
33. "And ____ himself in water" (Lev. 15:5)
36. "My heart's desire and prayer to God for ____ is, that they might be saved" (Rom. 10:1)
39. "One ____ stretched forth his hand. . .unto the fire" (Ezek. 10:7)
42. French article
43. Assistant, abbr.

44. "A virgin shall conceive. . .and shall call his name ____" (Isa. 7:14)
48. Biblical land: ____ of the Chaldees
49. "I am the true ____" (John 15:1)
51. "He ____ again the third day" (1 Cor. 15:4)
52. Spring month
53. Preposition
54. "His name shall be called ____" (Isa. 9:6)

DOWN

1. "For ____ is my witness" (Rom. 1:9)
2. Chemical suffix
3. "Every spirit that confesseth that Jesus Christ is come in the ____ is of God" (1 John 4:2)
4. "The coasts of ____" (Matt. 15:21)
5. "He that hath the Son hath ____" (1 John 5:12)
6. King of Bashan (Num. 21:33)
7. The damsel that opened the door for Peter (Acts 12:13)
8. Dental technician, abbr.
9. "That ye may know what is the hope of his ____" (Eph. 1:18)
10. "After the most straitest ____ of our religion I lived a Pharisee" (Acts 26:5)
12. "He that ____ not knoweth not God" (1 John 4:8)
16. "When for the time ye ought to be ____, ye have need that one teach you again" (Heb. 5:12)
18. "We which have believed do enter into ____" (Heb. 4:3)

20. American actor and humorist, initials
21. "Except I shall. . .put my finger into the print of the _____. . . , I will not believe" (John 20:25)
23. Jr.'s dad
24. "The Lamb that was _____" (Rev. 5:12)
28. Mary was a _____ when Christ was born
29. When you'll reach your destination, more or less, abbr.
30. Bachelor of Theology, abbr.
34. "Do not think that I will _____ you to the Father" (John 5:45)
35. "Come down, and _____ his son" (John 4:47)
37. Shade tree (Hos. 4:13)
38. "Take my yoke upon you, and _____ of me" (Matt. 11:29)
40. Habitual
41. Battery, abbr.
45. Kitten's cry
46. Biblical land (Gen. 4:16)
47. Before, poetic
49. South Carolina's neighbor to the north, abbr.
50. Neuter pronoun
52. Missouri University, abbr.

by Rebecca Souder

PUZZLE 48

ACROSS

1. "Except a man be born of ____ and of the Spirit, he cannot enter into the kingdom" (John 3:5)
5. Preposition
6. "Wisdom giveth ____" (Eccles. 7:12)
9. The son of Boaz (Matt. 1:5)
10. Two, prefix
11. Four, Rom. num.
12. Edge
13. Flesh-eater
16. "Let their table be a snare, and a ____" (Rom. 11:9)
18. Girl's name
19. "____. . .was wicked" (Gen. 38:7)
20. ____ Christian Anderson
21. "We remember the fish which we did eat freely in Egypt. . .and the leeks, and the ____, and the garlick" (Num. 11:5)
23. A celebration
25. Perform
26. Article
28. Osmium, chem. symbol
29. A deep breath
31. Taxis
32. "A serpent ____ him" (Amos 5:19)
33. Group of three
34. "I will not ____ out his name" (Rev. 3:5)
35. Single, prefix
36. Recover strength
37. "How long will it be ____ they attain to innocency?" (Hos. 8:5)
38. Executive order, abbr.
40. "I will ____ of mercy and judgment: unto thee, O Lord" (Ps. 101:1)

42. Library numbering system, abbr.
44. "There shall be no ____ on the vine" (Jer. 8:13)
48. Compass point
49. "As the ____ among thorns, so is my love among the daughters" (Song of Sol. 2:2)
50. "It is a ____ thing that the king requireth" (Dan. 2:11)
51. "For ____ so loved the world" (John 3:16)

DOWN

1. Value
2. Man who conspired against Moses (Num. 16:1)
3. Son of Esau (Gen. 36:11)
4. "Called the altar ____" (Josh. 22:34)
5. Pagiel's father (Num. 1:13)
6. "Why seek ye the ____ among the dead?" (Luke 24:5)
7. "Behold the ____ and the wood: but where is the lamb?" (Gen. 22:7)
8. "Whosoever believeth on him should not perish, but have ____ life" (John 3:16)
10. Bismuth, chem. symbol
14. Old Testament prophet
15. Person who lives next door—and also the person we are to love the same as we love ourselves
17. Science of the mind
22. Southern continent, abbr.
24. Cut of meat
25. Nimble
26. Story
27. This, Sp.
29. Casual walk

30. Hero of David's guard
    (1 Chron. 11:40)
31. Type of radio
32. Purchasing
39. "Break also the ____"
    (Amos 1:5)
41. New, prefix
43. 101, Rom. num.
45. Ma's mate
46. More, suffix
47. Compass point

by Cheryl Keiser

PUZZLE 49

ACROSS

1. Stepped
5. "Though ye _____ not me, believe the works" (John 10:38)
11. "His own _____ him not" (John 1:11)
13. Spoke
14. Bone, prefix
15. "A man sent from _____" (John 1:6)
17. Tissue plasminogen interceptor, abbr.
18. Seventh note of the musical scale
19. Doctor of Theology, abbr.
20. "The express _____ of his person" (Heb. 1:3)
22. Head, abbr.
23. Salvation Army, abbr.
24. Nickel, chem. symbol
25. "He gave his _____ begotten Son" (John 3:16)
27. The, Sp.
29. Preposition
31. "_____ gave names to all cattle" (Gen. 2:20)
33. "The _____ is the world" (Matt. 13:38)
35. "The Word _____ with God" (John 1:1)
37. French article
38. Canadian province, abbr.
40. New Testament, abbr.
41. "Full of _____ and truth" (John 1:14)
44. "_____ no man any thing" (Rom. 13:8)
47. Not down
48. "To whom be glory for _____" (2 Tim. 4:18)
49. "Go ye into all the _____" (Mark 16:15)
51. "Jesus _____ the Christ" (John 20:31)
52. That is, Lat. abbr.
53. Spirited
54. Spares
57. Doctor of Science, abbr.
58. "Sat down on the right _____ of the Majesty" (Heb. 1:3)
59. "Tempted like as we are, _____ without sin" (Heb. 4:15)

DOWN

1. Pledge
2. Dwelled
3. Fall month, abbr.
4. "Put off the old man with his _____" (Col. 3:9)
5. "In the _____ was the Word" (John 1:1)
6. Doeg was from this tribe (1 Sam. 21:7)
7. Exists
8. "I have never _____ any thing that is common or unclean" (Acts 10:14)
9. Very important person, abbr.
10. "Let us therefore follow after the things. . .wherewith one may _____ another" (Rom. 14:19)
12. Infinitesimal amount
16. District attorney, abbr.
21. "_____ ye therefore, and teach all nations" (Matt. 28:19)
26. "Behold the _____ of God!" (John 1:36)
28. "The _____ was given by Moses" (John 1:17)
29. "How shall ye believe, _____ I tell you of heavenly things?" (John 3:12)
30. Widemouthed pot

The crossword grid with numbered cells: 1, 2, 3, 4, 5, 6, 7, 8, 9, 10, 11, 12, 13, 14, 15, 16, 17, 18, 19, 20, 21, 22, 23, 24, 25, 26, 27, 28, 29, 30, 31, 32, 33, 34, 35, 36, 37, 38, 39, 40, 41, 42, 43, 44, 45, 46, 47, 48, 49, 50, 51, 52, 53, 54, 55, 56, 57, 58, 59

31. "Truly ye bear witness that ye ____ the deeds of your father" (Luke 11:48)

32. Name for Christ: the Son of ____

34. "Neither was any ____ in his mouth" (Isa. 53:9)

36. "____ to shew thyself approved" (2 Tim. 2:15)

39. The Anointed One

42. "After that he was ____ from the dead" (John 21:14)

43. "So is ____ one that is born of the Spirit" (John 3:8)

45. "The ____ was made flesh" (John 1:14)

46. Historic periods

50. Numbering system for library books, abbr.

55. Ex dividend, abbr.

56. Of age, Lat. abbr.

by Rebecca Souder

ACROSS

1. Pretty much
6. Off the cuff (2 words)
11. Expelled gas
12. Belonging to the earth
14. Radium, chem. symbol
15. Precious stone on the third row of the priest's breastplate (Exod. 28:19)
17. Western Canadian province, abbr.
18. All right
19. Annoyed
20. Short greeting
21. "I. . .have the ____ of hell and of death" (Rev. 1:18)
24. Creatures from outer space, abbr.
25. Slightly open
27. One who revises
29. "I was afraid, and went and hid thy ____ in the earth" (Matt. 25:25)
31. Peter once cut one off
32. Belonging to New York's largest island, abbr.
33. "The glory of the Lord ____ the house" (Ezek. 43:5)
36. First appearances
39. "Ye ____ men with burden grievous to be borne" (Luke 11:46)
40. Lemon beverage
42. "____ ____ a rod of an almond tree" (Jer. 1:11) (2 words)
43. Letter that follows el
44. Belonging to Mr. Rogers
46. A mate for Pa
47. Eastbound, abbr.
48. Cancel
49. Point, abbr.
50. Angry outburst
53. Man-made channels
56. Collapsed
57. Give off

DOWN

1. What the Mount Sinai did when the Lord descended
2. Biblical land: ____ of the Chaldees
3. Innings pitched, abbr.
4. "Lest he ____ my soul like a lion" (Ps. 7:2)
5. More nervous
6. Affirm
7. "Let us not love in word, neither in tongue; but in ____ and in truth" (1 John 3:18)
8. Living room, abbr.
9. Iridium, chem. symbol
10. "Dan. . .shall leap from ____" (Deut. 33:22)
11. Penniless
13. Part of a dress below the waist
16. Altitude, abbr.
22. "____ yourselves to the Lord" (2 Chron. 30:8)
23. Not fresh
25. A plausible excuse
26. Son of God and Son of man
28. Metal
30. Strong drink
33. Swift
34. Verse written in iambs
35. Mended socks
36. Figure out
37. Where Samuel grew up
38. "The four and twenty elders, which sat before God on their ____" (Rev. 11:16)
41. Where Daniel spent time with lions

44. Lose color
45. Shut hard
51. Royal Academy, abbr.
52. Audio-visual, abbr.
54. Negative
55. Preposition

ANSWERS

Puzzle 1

|1 A|L|T|A|R| |5 T|H|6 I|7 N|8 G|9 S|
|U| |10 B|U|11 S|H| |12 S|O|A|P|
|13 B|U|R|N|T| |14 I|15 R|A| |16 L|O|
|17 H|E| |18 A|S|A| |19 C|R|A|20 M|K|
|E| |21 O|H| |22 Y|23 A|K| |24 C|A|25 R|E|
|R| |26 R|A|27 M| |28 M|E| |29 I|N|N|
30 O	31 F		32 M	O	U	N	T	A	33 I	N	S
34 I	N		35 R		N		E		36 W
37 P	R	O	V	I	38 D	E		39 G	O	40 C	O
41 L	E	D		A		Y		E		42 S	L	O
43 A	D	E		44 E	45 E	L		46 L	A	D
C		47 E		48 I	S	H		49 A	S
50 E	A	R	L	Y			51 D	A	Y	S

Puzzle 2

1 A	A	R	2 O	N		5 W	E	A	V	E	R	S
11 B	D		12 N	O		13 A	D	D		14 T	A	R
15 B	A	16 B	Y		17 U	R		18 A	19 T	C
Y		20 O	X	21 E	N		22 S	P	I	23 C	E	24 S
25 A	W		V		26 P	I	T		O	E
27 M	A		28 E	29 V	E	N		30 R	31 U	L	E
32 O	F	33 F	E	R	I	N	G		34 R	E	D
35 S	P	P		E		36 P	37 A	T	E
E		38 C	H	39 E	40 R	41 U	B	I	M	S		42 S
43 S	44 T		45 O	N		46 S	E	47 I	X	I
48 O	L	D		49 G	O	50 L	D		51 S	I	N
52 A	I		53 Y	A		54 L	O	V	E		A
55 L	I	N	E	N		56 A	G	57 E	L	I

Puzzle 3

1 J	O	2 R	3 D	4 A	N		6 P	7 S	A	L	8 M	9 S
11 A	M	I	E	S		12 P	O	T		13 A	I	R
14 I	R	O	N		15 S	T	A	L	K	S
16 L	I	T	A	17 N	18 Y		19 T	I		20 E	21 T	A
O		22 R	A	I	23 M	E	N	24 T		L
R		25 D	I	A	P	E	R		26 T
27 E		28 U	M		E		29 A	30 R	31 R	O	W
32 R	33 S	A	34 C	35 K	S		36 K	A	P	H
37 O	H		38 N	I	N	39 E	V	E	H		E
40 M	A	41 G	I		D	42 E	L	A	Y		B
43 A	N		44 E	S	A	45 U		P	A	L
N		46 H	47 A	R	S	H	48 L	Y		C
49 S	W	E	E	T			50 T	E	R	A	H

Puzzle 4

1 A	B	R	A	H	A	M		A		8 A	H	9 I	10 J	11 A	12 H
13 B	A	A		14 O	15 B	A	D	I	A	16 H		17 N	O	T	E
18 E	L	I		19 S	E	L	A		20 C	21 A	D		S	L
22 D	A	N	I	E	L		V		23 E	Z	E	K	I	E	L
A		24 A	W	I		D	I	A
26 O	M	R	I		27 G	A	D		28 A	29 B	30 I	H	31 U	S
B		32 D	O	G		33 J	34 E	H	U	S		I
35 E	36 Z	37 R	38 A		39 D	E	U	40 E	L		41 Z	42 I	43 B	A
44 D	E	A	T	45 H		46 S	A	R	47 I		I	S	A	A	C
48 C	H	E	A	T			E	D		49 A	R
51 A	H	A		R		52 S	A	M	U	E	L		50 L	O	T
54 A	M	O	55 S		E	I	N		M		N
56 A	R		57 H	58 A	G	G	A	I		59 R	60 O	T
61 F	62 I	63 L	M		64 B	U	65 H		66 J	O	67 S	H	U	A
68 C	A	L	E	B		69 B	70 E		71 V	72 O	T	E		73 P	I
H		74 N	E	T		P		75 J	E	S	S	E	L

Puzzle 5

WATER · BEWARE · AMI · NCO · IRATE · LAMB · TOT · I · L · K · EARTH · HANDS · G · PIE · ASK · L · NEST · A · CT · LOT · ON · INCREASE · E · BOAZ · HE · NET · A · L · EYE · ADE · AC · END · ORAL · DASH · AI · U · G · B · B · E · LINEN · RULER · ALE · GOD · ONES

Puzzle 6

FOREHEAD · HAND · ICI · E · NAVEL · E · NEB · EACH · MPH · GAS · LLAMA · O · EN · E · EI · I · OR · R · EDGE · ACTION · BY · XV · ELL · TEETH · EL · LOW · O · SHOULDER · NE · NO · ULTI · GANG · GUMMY · PAST · J · US · B · ESS · BAA · ETC · AM · HEAD · W

Puzzle 7

INCISE · TRANCE · STATES · RAMOTH · BETHLEHEM · BE · M · TEN · N · HO · ASS · SS · MOOCH · BAD · ACTION · HERALD · AERO · REST · SPEEDS · ROTTEN · N · PEP · SELED · ETA · YD · W · REL · K · HB · PETITIONS · ARABIA · ENOUGH · DAMSEL · DETEST

Puzzle 8

ROSEOFSHARON · IN · N · SHY · OA · GOODSHEPHERD · H · DIP · E · IA · THETRUTH · LAMB · ET · EY · HO · II · U · O · K · SONOFMAN · USED · RETE · LD · SONOFGOD · CPA · R · OXO · KS · HN · TEAR · DOVE · SAT · N · D · R · WAY · E · MORNINGSTAR

Puzzle 9

WORKMAN · SWORD · H · AMI · ETA · PRO · ISRAELS · MME · I · ERNEST · ONAN · ED · T · T · O · MING · ER · A · PREENS · AVENGE · E · SANG · SON · EL · TT · SO · ATOM · M · TR · SETH · I · NATHAN · LE · NOD · EIGHT · EN · ON · ABASE · ULVA · ESTHER · DAMPEN

Puzzle 10

DARKNESS · BLOW · ISU · IRES · EACH · VIL · GRASS · NCA · IDE · H · T · D · L · DE · ETERNAL · FE · E · HS · GO · ROARS · DEEP · GOD · REU · DAY · SEED · IF · LIV · EAT · ATE · ITEMS · FOWL · D · F · NOT · LIGHTS · S · EAST · FES · AAUP · T · EARTH · TREE

Puzzle 11

```
C A N A . C A P . . S T A R
O R E N . O U R . H I R E .
P E S O . U R E . A M A N .
. A S T O N I S H M E N T .
. . H I T . . E E E . . . .
N A V E L . A N N . . W I N
E V E R . G A T . D A R A .
T A X . I R A . J E S U S .
. . A R I . B E L . . . . .
C O N F I S C A T I O N . .
A L O T . L A B . G N A T .
M I N E . E N E . H E M I .
P O O R . D E L . T R E S .
```

Puzzle 12

```
D O R C A S . E A S T E R .
E L U L . A N S W E R . . .
. . T O . . S A T I R E . E
. T H U M B S . Y A P . . B
H A . D E A T H . . . . B E
A R K . A T E . . G I E R .
I R A . T H A N K I N G . .
R I T E . . L E A F . . S O
Y E T . B R E A D T H . . G
. D A Y . A T R E S I A . .
A . T E A C H . S . L I E .
B E H A V E . A H . L A Y .
E D . R E S T S . . S H E .
```

Puzzle 13

```
H E Z E K I A H . . J U D A H
A . I V M . A G A B U S . . B
B . M A N A E N . T . . A S A
A I R . E G . A P H I A H . M
K . I D L E . N A . L O W L Y
K A . A L . L I O N . U R O .
U N I T . E S A U . J O R A M
K N H A L . H . S E P . . . O
A D A M I . T . R U S H . . L
H . A N . J E T H R O S . . .
A X . A M E E . B . E L O I .
M . N O A H . R . J O E L . .
A N A . . R . A N N A . D E B T
N E H E M I A H . M E A L . H
C O M E . J O N A H . R . H A M
```

Puzzle 14

```
S H A L L . V . A S P . . .
. E L I . P A S T U R E S . .
. T E A R . T . . P U S H . .
M A . . D E L I S . N E E . .
E V I L . P . L I F E . . . P
R . A . F A I L . L . . . . H
C O M F O R T . . T A B L E .
Y F . O R E . M . . Y E A R .
F A R . S . E H . . R O D . .
A . D E A T H . O N E . . . .
V . V . E M U . . D U E . . .
G R E E N . A S S T . . S R .
. T A R O . D W E L L E R . .
```

Puzzle 15

```
S A L T . A E N E A S . . . C
A G A I N S T . . . . . . L O
I R O N . S A C R E D . . . R
N E D . H U M P . T Y . . I .
T E I L . R . D . A N O N . .
. C A M E L . E . A N T . . H
S H E M . I S L E S . . . . .
C . A E D I L E . E T U I . .
R E . N I . A P P L Y . . A .
I N S T R U C T . . . . O N .
B A T . T N . E L D E R S . .
E N E M Y . S T A I R . . . .
S . M E . D I S P E R S E . .
```

Puzzle 16

```
R E N D . I N T O . . E K E .
O V E R . F O U R . . R E D .
D E T E R . T B A . . R E I .
. A I R . A C C E P T . . . .
T R I M M E D . L A D . . . .
I O N S . P E T E R . . E H .
M A N . M A L E S . . A D E .
E D . R O Y A L . . U V E A .
. S U R . Y E A R E N D . . .
L A M E N T . M U G . . . . .
A H A . I R E . K E N A N . .
O I L . N U T S . N A I N . .
S O L . G E A R . . T Y R E .
```

Puzzle 17

M	A	R		S	A	I	D		P	A	D	S

Row 1: MAR · SAID · PADS
Row 2: ARE · IMNA · ARIA
Row 3: DAVID · AND · REAL
Row 4: EDEN · ATALE
Row 5: ISRED · HERO
Row 6: DOES · PARAFFIN
Row 7: EON · BARON · IRE
Row 8: ANDHARPS · GNAW
Row 9: ANTS · POINT
Row 10: SPARK · ALAS
Row 11: HAND · JONATHAN
Row 12: AGEE · OREN · EWE
Row 13: HEWN · BETS · DEE

Puzzle 18

Row 1: SHEPHERD · LARD
Row 2: HOPE · VALLEY · E
Row 3: AU · EDIT · ENE · A
Row 4: DS · PILE · ASSET
Row 5: OER · N · DAD · AH
Row 6: W · EVER · NEVER · R
Row 7: ASA · EXOTIC · D
Row 8: OATS · D · IHS · CW
Row 9: I · OT · YEN · ACRE
Row 10: LGR · SEATS · EEL
Row 11: RENT · TENT · EL
Row 12: BETTER · S · ASPS
Row 13: UGH · PASTURES

Puzzle 19

Row 1: ABOMINABLE · ROGUE
Row 2: CAB · COW · U · RGA · U
Row 3: KNIFE · EASTER · LET
Row 4: NILE · A · NT · VANITY
Row 5: O · TOBIT · DEW · L · C
Row 6: WEST · IDOL · BETH
Row 7: LB · EYE · OAK · E · U
Row 8: EBER · SHIRT · PS
Row 9: D · USE · AR · IVORY
Row 10: GIN · IDDO · M · R
Row 11: EU · JESSE · N · BAAL
Row 12: ACHAN · TIE · HMO
Row 13: ASH · MT · TROAS · IN
Row 14: A · HEIR · YARN · ADD
Row 15: APE · SLOW · NESTS · O
Row 16: SHEM · EDEN · B · SUN

Puzzle 20

Row 1: MULTIPLY · SANS
Row 2: ANOINTS · SHIRT
Row 3: SWINE · SWEAR
Row 4: TIN · XI · END · PA
Row 5: ENSNARE · DOG · M
Row 6: RD · CRAG · WARS
Row 7: A · TIGER · DE
Row 8: SILK · GLEAN · D
Row 9: IDLE · AE · NAMED
Row 10: NOD · TS · STEER
Row 11: FLEECE · OH · MA
Row 12: US · SO · GAMA · EM
Row 13: L · HOLON · NODS

Puzzle 21

Row 1: PI · BA · HEBRON
Row 2: REARS · OAU · I
Row 3: I · RE · JONATHAN
Row 4: ETTA · AB · SHED
Row 5: SW · DAVID · RUE
Row 6: TOO · SELF
Row 7: S · GOLIATH · LT
Row 8: UP · VI · Y · E · A
Row 9: C · SLING · AMT
Row 10: ADA · ELIAB · A
Row 11: VALIANT · NOR
Row 12: ELM · LE · HERE
Row 13: SOLOMON · RES

Puzzle 22

Row 1: WALKETH · STAND
Row 2: HEAD · RIVERS · O
Row 3: A · DUE · AERIE
Row 4: TO · SEE · ATE · T
Row 5: SHEEP · WM · CH
Row 6: O · LA · SITTETH
Row 7: EDIT · IN · EV · AM
Row 8: VE · AND · LEAF
Row 9: EL · C · ALS · FN
Row 10: RIGHTEOUS · I
Row 11: GHARRY · NG · G
Row 12: WHAT · SETFORTH
Row 13: ATT · Z · FRUIT

Puzzle 23

NERO · ACTS · ARK
ALIT · BARE · HOE
NIGH · CREEPING
ASHER · EARL
TRADED · AFAR
ACE · TAN · STOLE
BOOGEY · CHERAN
BLUES · THE · TED
EASE · THIRTY
SARI · DODAI
COVENANT · RAID
ONE · NIKE · TYRE
WOE · ELSE · ESSE

Puzzle 24

OPHIR · WALKING
PE · HALO · EAR · L
PASSION · A · ERA
R · L · NOD · SP · D
ESAU · MENTION
S · ITS · RE · ZIT
SANCTIFIED · GO
D · AU · SETH
COVER · LK · PATH
ORPHAN · STP
ME · I · FATHER
BRUISE · SA · EO
SSR · ESTABLISH

Puzzle 25

CORNELIUS · PETER
ONE · DU · I · IRAN
REST · KILL · MART
NS · HUE · TALL · E
SIMON · J · SAINTS · L
M · MAGOG · NP · HA
LUNA · SEND · BY · OZ
SOSTHENES · R · ASA
C · PI · JOHN · R
A · MATTHEW · UK · U
IN · U · OH DEAR · S
AUGUSTUS · EA · EL
P · AN · WA · SHOWED
HI · JAMES · AN · GA
ANNA · ROE · INLAW · Y
SOS · BARTHOLOMEW

Puzzle 26

ED · SLIDE · AIAH
ROTTEN · LAID · E
HOT · FIND · UR
SHIP · LAUD · ONE
HIS · VOID · CAN
IT · MOAN · SARID
E · MOUNTAINS · E
SEATS · NOTE · WE
ORE · DENS · HAD
ANY · NOSE · PASS
IS · ANTS · ART
J · TREE · ERASER
AMOK · DELAY · NA

Puzzle 27

CONSIDER · ARLO
ANYA · AARON · IN
RC · LENT · TOFU
PER · M · BASTES
E · REPENTS · HL
NT · E · ASP · NI
TENORS · WIND
E · IDOL · TRI · ER
RIVER · OA · NH · O
N · FIR · DO · P
OTHNIEL · TOWEL
GRAVAMEN · WIRE
SATAN · DESSERT

Puzzle 28

CHAP · MID · CHAS
AERO · ETE · OOLA
SLEW · RES · VAIN
SIDE PERPLEXED
RID · IAN
REEDS · ST PAULS
NASO · DIE · NSAS
STAMMER · STABS
IAL · SOB
ABUNDANT GRACE
RONI · YEA · ALAS
ANNO · ERI · KISS
MEIN · DIN · ETTE

Puzzle 29

```
M O U N T A I N       P O T
  E     S I       T W O   L   E
A N G E L S     O     B A K E
  B   A     O F     P I E
R A T T E D     R A I N E D
O N E     L O T   B       P A
A D     G O M O R R A H       U
D     U R N   M I A   E G G
    D I E     M     H U R       H
  O   A     E S C A P E       T
W E N T     N A M         H E
  A   O L E     L O   I S     R
C I T Y       T H O S E       S
```

Puzzle 30

```
C H U R C H       M O R S E L
R A R E     I     W I   M N O
A R N O L D       L     O D D
  S P     D     R E     R U G
H S T     M E T E D       E R E
        F I N E D     W   E
G   D O G     N     T E R S E
R E   G H O S T     B E       X
E V E   T R E E         M A P
A I D   Y     A D I N       R
T L C     S E P A R A T E
L     I O U     O N A N       S
Y O U N G E S T         N T H S
```

Puzzle 31

```
P R O S P E R S     M A R C
R E R A N     I N S E T     A
I I   C   A M   O D       T
M G   K   A M O R I T E S
A N I S E   O   B U S     P
T E N     I O N   O M E G A
E T     D G     O N     T O W
    H I K E   C A N     S R
S   F O R S A K E     E G O
H O   R   H I S     A   O N
E L E A Z E R     A W A N A
I D A H O     O R D E R     N
K   T S A R     B E D     S S
```

Puzzle 32

```
A S A     J I B B     A B L E
T A M     E S A U     S L A T
E M I S S A R Y     H U R T
    N E S T     G E E S E
I N A W E     B A L E
D A D S     J O S A P H A T
O N A     D A R E D     E R A
L A B O U R E R     E R I N
    T E S S     C L O A K
E I G H T     S L I D
T O R E     N E H E M I A H
A T E R     A R E A     A L E
S A Y S     H E W N     S I R
```

Puzzle 33

```
B R O T H E R     O F T E N
L     E N R A G E     E T A
E Y E S     R   R     N O T
S O R T S     H A N D       I
  R A     L O V E     N O
E S   M O     N E W S   A N
D I N E     O     A L M S
  S A N C T U A R Y     E
S U T T E R M O S T     S
P I G     M     A S   A R K
I   H E L P     Z E A L     E
N A T E     L I E     E Y E
E T   L E N D O R     E T
```

Puzzle 34

```
G E N E S I S     P I L A T E     J
A N I     P S     F I R E     G E
Z E C H A R I A H     F I N D     W
A   O I L     N U     F E S T U S
  A D   P S     L I E     G O D   R
S T E P H E N     P L E A D     R
  E M   A T   G   I     R A B B I
B   U S E     F A   X   C E A   N
A S S   U R I M     O H     R K
R U   S A L A D     J U S T U S
N E S T     T L     S D I
A   T R O P H I M U S     M A T
B A   U   I E     C A E S A R
A B S E N T     L A K E     S E T H
S E E     R T   D     M   U S A
    E P A P H R O D I T U S     M
```

Puzzle 35

¹H	²E	I	³R	⁴S		⁵M	A	R	B	L	E	⁹E

Row 1: H E I R S — M A R B L E — E
Row 2: ¹⁰E A — ¹¹Y O K E ¹²/¹³ — ¹⁴F A A — D
Row 3: L — ¹⁵F E L L O W — ¹⁶W ¹⁷H A — I
Row 4: ¹⁸P A N ¹⁹ D — ²⁰M O R A ²¹ ²²D C
Row 5: ²³E N — ²⁴T I M — ²⁵R A B B I T ²⁶
Row 6: ²⁷R Y — ²⁸R E — ²⁹K G — ³⁰I S
Row 7: S — ³¹W O R K — ³²E G O ³⁰ — ³⁴C E ³⁵
Row 8: ³⁶L O U — ³⁷G R E W — ³⁸I L
Row 9: ³⁹L A U G H ⁴⁰H — ⁴¹S D — ⁴²P D
Row 10: A — ⁴³L H A S A ⁴⁴⁴⁵ — ⁴⁶I S L E ⁴⁷
Row 11: ⁴⁸B A D ⁴⁹ — ⁵⁰P R I S O N E R ⁵¹
Row 12: ⁵²O X — ⁵³P E ⁵⁴ ⁵⁵I R — ⁵⁶F U S S
Row 13: R — ⁵⁷C I T I Z E N — B

Puzzle 36

Row 1: ¹H O L Y — ³G H O S T — ⁷U R
Row 2: A — ⁸H A — ⁹A A R O N
Row 3: ¹⁰N A R R O W ¹¹ — T I — ¹²I A ¹³
Row 4: D — ¹⁴D A N — ¹⁵H E B R O N
Row 5: ¹⁶S B ¹⁷ ¹⁸Y E A R S ¹⁹ U — ²⁰N E
Row 6: ²¹E R ²² S E ²³ L — W
Row 7: ²³A G E — ²⁴T ²⁵R E S P A S S ²⁷²⁸
Row 8: ²⁹M A — ³⁰J — ³¹O D E — ³²T O E S
Row 9: ³⁴T W O ³⁵ O — C I — ³⁶W E
Row 10: ³⁷W — ³⁸I T — ³⁹T O R T O I S E ⁴⁰
Row 11: H — D — E — ⁴¹N M
Row 12: ⁴²I R O N — ⁴³N — ⁴⁴M U T T ⁴⁵⁴⁶ — ⁴⁷R E D ⁴⁸
Row 13: P — ⁴⁹W O — ⁵⁰A P O — I — O

Puzzle 37

Row 1: ¹I N V I T A T I O N — ⁹O F ¹⁰
Row 2: ¹¹N A — ¹²N I — ¹³O T T O — ¹⁴D O
Row 3: ¹⁵T H O U G H T S ¹⁶¹⁷ — ¹⁸Y O U
Row 4: E — ¹⁹F R E T S — ²⁰O F ²¹ ²²R N
Row 5: R — ²³E R S — ²⁴C H R I S T ²⁵
Row 6: ²⁶C O L D — H — ²⁹A N
Row 7: ³⁰E M U — ³¹U — ³²S O — ³³I D E A
Row 8: ³⁶S R — ³⁷³⁸S C A R E D — ³⁹A N
Row 9: ⁴⁰S I S T E R ⁴¹ U — ⁴²B — ⁴⁶
Row 10: I — ⁴³I R E ⁴⁴⁴⁵S L E A V E
Row 11: ⁴⁷O V E R ⁴⁸⁴⁹ — ⁵⁰A E ⁵¹ A — ⁵²N O N
Row 12: ⁵³N A M E — ⁵⁴S L A M — ⁵⁵A W N
Row 13: ⁵⁶R E D E E M — ⁵⁷B A L S A

Puzzle 38

Row 1: ¹S C H I S M — ³C O M M I T ⁶⁷
Row 2: ⁸O H — ⁹I O T A — ¹⁰I N
Row 3: ¹¹D I N E — L — ¹²C R E C H E ¹³ ¹⁴
Row 4: ¹⁵I N — ¹⁶G A T H — ¹⁷P E E R
Row 5: ¹⁸R — ¹⁹O D — ²⁰E P H — R
Row 6: ²¹A M O Z — ²²A H ²³²⁴ — ²⁵A H E M ²⁶
Row 7: L — ²⁷B I L H A H — ²⁸H E ²⁹
Row 8: ³⁰G O O — O — ³¹L E G — ³²R O C ³³³⁴³⁵
Row 9: U — ³⁶L N — ³⁷Y O R E — ³⁸O T A
Row 10: ³⁹M O O — ⁴⁰D E — ⁴¹H I D ⁴² — R
Row 11: ⁴³A B O M I N A T I O N ⁴⁴⁴⁵⁴⁶
Row 12: ⁴⁷M O T E ⁴⁸ E — ⁴⁹U Z — ⁵⁰A G A
Row 13: ⁵¹A S H — ⁵²A N A N I A S — L

Puzzle 39

Row 1: ¹C O M E — ⁵A I — ⁶T R U S T ⁷⁸⁹¹⁰
Row 2: ¹¹H I N N O M ¹² — ¹³H A P P Y
Row 3: ¹⁴A L — ¹⁵T N — ¹⁶W A Y ¹⁷ — ¹⁸S A P
Row 4: N — ¹⁹C E L L O S — ²⁰L — ²¹R E
Row 5: ²²G L O R Y ²³ R — ²⁴F I R E ²⁵
Row 6: ²⁶E I — ²⁷²⁸B E L I E V E T H ²⁹ ³⁰
Row 7: ³¹R E D — ³²³³E N D S — ³⁴E C H O
Row 8: ³⁵S T I N G ³⁶ — ³⁷L A T E — L
Row 9: ³⁸H E R O D — ³⁹E — ⁴⁰H I N D ⁴¹
Row 10: ⁴²P — ⁴³D A T E S ⁴⁴ — ⁴⁵P ⁴⁶V E
Row 11: ⁴⁷I N ⁴⁸ — ⁴⁹A C H I E V E ⁵⁰ ⁵¹
Row 12: ⁵²C O N F E S S E D ⁵³⁵⁴⁵⁵ — ⁵⁶D E N
Row 13: ⁵⁷A S C E N D E D — ⁵⁸R D

Puzzle 40

Row 1: ¹M I N T — ⁴F I T C H E S ⁸
Row 2: ⁹U M — ¹⁰E V E R ¹¹¹² — ¹³O D E — A
Row 3: ¹⁴S P I K E N A R D ¹⁵ — ¹⁶R A F ¹⁷
Row 4: T — V — R — ¹⁸N Y A L A ¹⁹ — F
Row 5: ²⁰A L O E S ²¹ — ²²K E Y S — ²³U R
Row 6: ²⁴R O R — ²⁵E V I ²⁶ — ²⁷O N O
Row 7: ²⁸D R Y — ²⁹A N I S E ³⁰³¹³² — ³³E N
Row 8: D — ³⁴H I — ³⁵C U M M I N ³⁶
Row 9: ³⁷M — ³⁸A Y — ³⁹M E — ⁴⁰E N D S
Row 10: ⁴¹Y A M S ⁴² — ⁴³I N C E N S E ⁴⁴
Row 11: ⁴⁵R Y E S — ⁴⁶S U D — ⁴⁷D I ⁴⁸
Row 12: ⁴⁹R E N O — ⁵⁰S E R B ⁵¹ — ⁵²T C
Row 13: H — ⁵³S P A M — ⁵⁴S P I C E

Puzzle 41

```
P H A R I S E E S . S O N
U . P A . . L E V I T E
B R O G A N . D . A B B I
L A S S . T . E C L . . G
I N T . . E . R E U M A H
C I A S . N G . R E . O B
A N T S . C A R E S . . O
N E E . P E Z . A . E M U
. . S . . A B L A T E R
P E O P L E . R . N . N
E S S A Y . E N D I T E
A S H N A H . A O R T A S
S E A S . A . D . E E L S
```

Puzzle 42

```
P E R F U M E R . B A K E
A N Y O N E . H O O F S
I G . U D O . O V A . . I
N R . N E W . D E T O U R
T A . D R . B A R B E R S
I V E . X U . U . G
N I T R E . R E F I N E R
G N A S H I N G . L A D E
. G B . F . . O D . . D
M . S O . W E A V I N G
I T . . E L N I N O . G
T E N T M A K I N G . G A
T A I L O R . M E . G O D
```

Puzzle 43

```
G I F T . N O T . T R U E
O . L I G H T . B O R N
D W E L T . G E M . D W
. O S E . G I R L . T O O
H R H . N A I L .
E L . R E C E I V E D
A D A M . E V . I V
R . B A A L S . E . N E W
D A R K N E S S . E R O
. R E E S T . O S S . Y R
B E A R W I T N E S S . T
O N S . E T O . T R U T H
W A T E R . C H . N A Y
```

Puzzle 44

```
S H E P H E R D . H . T A
W I N E . U . A G A B U S
O R D A I N . R U L E R S
R E E K . U N K N O W N
D . D E A C O N . A S K
. P . D H . E D A R . I
D I E . A S P S . M E . N
E G Y P T . A S H . A G
B . E . E A R . A M E N D
O B S E R V E . M . T O
R E . G . A N I M A L . M
A A R O N . T . E D I T
H U R . A S S U R A N C E
```

Puzzle 45

```
C A T T L E . F . S A
R A I N S . F O R M . E R
E . E T D . I R E . L E T
A P S . C R E A T E D
T I . F R O M . R U
U C A . W A T E R S
R O S E S . M O R N I N G
E T . A R E . I N T O
. B E G I N N I N G . O
S E A S . T O . G I R D
S T A R . E . T D . N O
A U S T E R E . A . G O D
W . T H I R D . Y E . F E
```

Puzzle 46

```
H O L Y . G H O S T . U R
A . O . H A . A A R O N
N A R R O W . T R I . I A
D . D A N . H E B R O N
S B . Y E A R . E U . N E
. E R . S E . L A . W
A G E . T R E S P A S S
M A . J . O D E . T I E S
. T W O . O . C I . W E
W . I T . T O R T O I S E
H O D . P E . N M
I R O N . M U T T . R E D
P . W O R M S . O B I . O
```

Puzzle 47

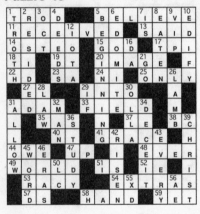

Puzzle 48

Puzzle 49

Puzzle 50

BIBLE
Crosswords
Collection #10

Compiled and Edited by
Ellyn Sanna

BARBOUR
PUBLISHING, INC.
Uhrichsville, Ohio

Published by Barbour Publishing, Inc.
P.O. Box 719
Uhrichsville, Ohio 44683
http://www.barbourbooks.com

Member of the
Evangelical Christian
Publishers Association

Printed in the United States of America.

BIBLE
Crosswords
Collection #10

PUZZLE 1

by Sissy Magnusson

ACROSS

1. The poor godly man in Christ's parable (Luke 16:20)
6. This liquid when new is not put in old bottles (Mark 2:22)
9. Printer's measure
10. Burying this was a mistake (Matt. 25:15–28)
13. Foolish man built his house on this (Matt. 7:46)
14. Half-way
15. Before, prefix
17. The Lord promised that though our sins be scarlet, they shall be white _____ snow
18. Bear-like animal related to the raccoon
20. Each, abbr.
21. Jesus is God's only begotten (John 3:16)
23. Jesus told a story about 5 wise and 5 foolish (Matt. 25:1–2)
25. Hello
26. Underling
27. Shade tree (Hos. 4:13)
29. What the disciples fished with (Matt. 13:47)
30. Finished first
32. City in the Netherlands famous for its cheese
33. No one puts this kind of cloth into an old garment (Mark 2:21)
34. A day's wage for a hired laborer (Matt. 20:2)
36. The enemy sowed these among the wheat (Matt. 13:25)
38. Thanks, Br.
39. Discharged a firearm
41. Hush!
42. Encountered
45. Egyptian sun god
47. Full of wonder
49. We shouldn't put this under a bushel (Mark 4:21)
52. Sick
54. The wise man built on this (Luke 6:48)
55. In Christ's story, the father threw a party for this son (Luke 15:11–32)

DOWN

1. The shepherd left the 99 for this (Matt. 18:11–12) (2 words)
2. Town in Judah (Josh. 15:37)
3. No ifs, _____, or buts
4. Salt Lake's state, abbr.
5. The Jews ostracized these people (John 4:9)
6. Jesus told a parable about a king who invited people to this kind of celebration
7. Surrounded by
8. Normal temperature and pressure, abbr.
11. A dialect
12. Biblical term for yeast (Matt. 13:33)
16. Do over again, prefix
18. Yearned
19. Article that precedes a vowel
22. The wise took this for their lamps (Matt. 25:4)
23. Jesus spoke of laborers in this place (Matt. 20:1)
24. One who scatters seed (Mark 4:3)
28. "A certain _____ made a great supper" (Luke 14:16)
31. In debt

33. Nathan, for short
35. Bible part that contains the Gospels, Epistles, and Revelation, abbr.
36. Pulled
37. "True worshippers ____ worship the Father in spirit and in truth" (John 4:23)
40. Laughter syllable
43. Environment, prefix
44. Tactical Air Command, abbr.
46. European mountain
48. Delve
50. "Unforgettable" Cole, first initials
51. Son of Jose (Luke 3:28–29)
53. Californian city, abbr.

by Joyce Handzo

ACROSS

1. "Behold I make all things ____"
   (Rev. 21:5)
2. "Praise him for his mighty ____"
   (Ps. 150:2)
5. Spheres or heavenly bodies
9. "Why make ye this ____ and
   weep?" (Mark 5:39)
10. "I will ____ a place for my
    people" (1 Chron. 17:9)
12. Recreational vehicle, abbr.
13. "The kingdom of heaven is ____
    hand" (Matt. 4:17)
15. "His teeth shall be set on ____"
    (Jer. 31:30)
16. Southeast, abbr.
18. Let ____ esteem other better
    than themselves (Phil. 2:3)
19. Registered nurse, abbr.
21. "____ so, come Lord Jesus"
    (Rev. 22:20)
22. "The Lord is my ____"
    (Heb. 13:6)
25. "____ and prepare the Passover"
    (Luke 22:8)
27. "Adam called his wife's name
    ____" (Gen. 3:20)
28. "I send an ____ before thee"
    (Exod. 23:20)
30. "Be ____ to maintain good
    works" (Titus 3:8)
33. British Thermal Unit, abbr.
34. "By which it had gone down
    in the ____ of Ahaz"
    (2 Kings 20:11)
35. New York, abbr.
36. "Thou shalt bind this ____
    of scarlet thread"
    (Josh. 2:18)

38. "For ____ are called but few are
    chosen" (Matt. 22:14)
40. Education, abbr.
41. "He maketh them also to ____
    like a calf" (Ps. 29:6)
43. "This is my beloved ____"
    (Matt. 17:5)
45. "His soul shall dwell at ____"
    (Ps. 25:13)
47. "Though an ____ should encamp
    against me, my heart shall not
    fear" (Ps. 27:3)
49. North America, abbr.
51. Professional, abbr.
53. A post erected by certain
    American Indians
55. A book of Psalms
56. A yearning

DOWN

1. "This is the ____ that ye have
   heard" (1 Kings 1:45)
2. The year of our Lord, Lat. abbr.
3. A tutor or instructor
4. "I have not found ____ great
   faith" (Luke 7:9)
5. "The ____ number of them"
   (Num. 3:48)
6. Worthless piece of cloth
7. "And he came and touched the
   ____" (Luke 7:14)
8. Shipping Note, abbr.
9. "____ not yourselves"
   (Rom. 12:19)
11. "The plowman shall overtake the
    ____" (Amos 9:13)
14. Definite article
17. "For it was now ____"
    (Acts 4:3)
20. "They had but ____ set the
    watch" (Judg. 7:19)

23. "_____ perfect gift is from above" (James 1:17)
24. Referee, abbr.
26. "_____ things are passed away" (2 Cor. 5:17)
28. "He is _____ also to save them" (Heb. 7:25)
29. A firearm
30. A synthetic gum used in medicine
31. Alabama, abbr.
32. "Woe is me! for I am _____" (Isa. 6:5)
37. Curved shape
39. Vicious

42. "Neither was any thing _____ secret" (Mark 4:22)
44. "For there is none other _____" (Acts 4:12)
46. A king of Judah
48. Moses sprinkled the blood upon Aaron's great _____ (Exod. 29:20)
50. Associated Press, abbr.
52. A prefix meaning to do over
54. Tennessee, abbr.

PUZZLE 3

by Mary Ann Freeman

ACROSS

1. "____ the just shall live by faith" (Heb. 10:38)
4. Breakfast food that goes with Noah's son (Gen. 5:32)
8. "____ without ceasing" (1 Thess. 5:17)
12. Dentists' group
13. Soccer great
14. Worn in a religious painting
15. "They neither sow ____ reap" (Luke 12:24)
16. No to a Scot
17. Last word in the Bible (Rev. 22:21)
18. Site of final conflict (Rev. 16:16)
22. Hath, in modern English
23. University in Carbondale, IL, abbr.
24. FL from TN, direction
26. Abraham's nephew (Gen. 14:12)
29. "She gave me of the tree, and I ____ eat" (Gen. 3:12)
31. What the lame man did (Acts 3:8)
33. Woodwind instrument
35. "____ thou on my right hand" (Matt. 22:44)
37. "Honey in the carcase of the ____" (Judg. 14:8)
38. "Get thee behind me, ____" (Matt. 16:23)
40. Time period
42. Subway system
43. ____ Salvador
44. Sun in Madrid
46. Balaam's Mr. Ed (Num. 22:28)
48. Luke's penpal (Acts 1:1)
53. "There is ____ good but one" (Matt. 19:17)
56. Canterbury's religious leader, abbr.
57. "Ye ____ the light of the world" (Matt. 5:14)
58. Pitcher
59. "Obedient by word and ____" (Rom. 15:18)
61. Missing soldier
62. Adolescent
63. Figures
64. Woman's malady

DOWN

1. Wendy's dog
2. "____ of a sweet smell" (Phil. 4:18)
3. "The flesh of the child waxed ____" (2 Kings 4:34)
4. Long play video tape setting, abbr.
5. Joseph's story told here
6. "A wise son maketh a ____ father" (Prov. 10:1)
7. What the sower sowed (Matt. 13:4)
8. Anna's father (Luke 2:36)
9. Took Isaac's place (Gen. 22:13)
10. Pub drink
11. Hither, thither, and ____
19. "____, Lord GOD" (Jer. 1:6)
20. Zilpah's lad (Gen. 30:11)
21. "Thou anointest my head with ____" (Ps. 23:5)
24. "Not having ____, or wrinkle" (Eph. 5:27)
25. Sicilian volcano
26. "He that loveth his life shall ____ it" (John 12:25)
27. Joktan's son (Gen. 10:28)
28. Child
30. "Appointed unto men once to ____" (Heb. 9:27)

32. Direct
34. Magi saw star in this sky (Matt. 2:2)
36. Stuck
39. Japanese drama
41. "He planted an ____, and the rain doth nourish it" (Isa. 44:14)
45. "____ ____ quiet and peaceable life" (1 Tim. 2:2) (2 words)
47. Yes to Julio
49. David's grandpa (Ruth 4:22)
50. "Thy word is a ____ unto my feet" (Ps. 119:105)
51. Used to cast lots (Num. 27:21)
52. Red and Dead
53. Kingdom of heaven is like one (Matt. 13:47)
54. "____ no man any thing" (Rom. 13:8)
55. Maiden name
60. Document signed, abbr.

PUZZLE 4

by Elizabeth B. Smith

ACROSS

1. Definite article
3. Jewess who became queen (Esther 2:17)
7. Eastern state, abbr.
8. "All that handle the _____, . . .shall come down from their ships" (Ezek. 27:29)
11. "Upon thy belly shalt thou _____" (Gen. 3:14)
13. "Disciples believed _____ him" (John 2:11)
14. Judah's wife (Gen. 38:12)
16. Naomi changed her name to _____ (Ruth 1:20)
19. "He said, Behold, I am _____, Lord" (Acts 9:10)
20. Enoch's son (Gen. 4:18)
21. "I _____ no pleasant bread" (Dan. 10:3)
23. Moses' mother (Exod. 6:20)
27. Mid-west state, abbr.
29. "Ye have not chosen _____, but I have chosen you" (John 15:16)
30. "Neither do the _____ understand" (Job 32:9)
32. Wife of Nabal (1 Sam. 25:3)
35. Old card game
36. "The counsel of the Lord, that _____ stand" (Prov. 19:21)
38. This woman hid spies on her roof (Josh. 2:1)
41. He cried unto the Lord his God (2 Chron. 14:11)
42. "Father said, "Let us _____, and be merry" (Luke 15:23)
44. Samson told her everything (Judg. 16:18)
47. Judah's daughter-in-law (Gen. 38:11)
49. Hodiah was his sister (1 Chron. 4:19)
50. Short greeting

DOWN

2. Angel spoke to her (Gen. 21:17)
3. Was made from a rib (Gen. 2:22; 3:20)
4. "Wisdom is _____ high for a fool" (Prov. 24:7)
5. Mother of Samuel (1 Sam. 1:20)
6. Judah's son (Gen. 38:3)
9. "_____ rose up hastily, . . .they followed" (John 11:31)
10. Put the nail in Sisera's temple (Judg. 4:21)
12. Plural of os
14. Queen of _____ heard of Solomon's fame (1 Kings 10:1)
15. Abraham left the land of _____ (Gen. 11:31)
16. Sister of Aaron (Exod. 15:20)
17. Paid announcement
18. Ruth's mother-in-law (Ruth 1:22)
22. Topographical Engineer, abbr.
24. Single room in prison
25. David's wife (2 Sam. 3:5)
26. Eastern state, abbr.
27. Saul gave her to David (1 Sam. 18:27)
28. King of Bashan (Num. 21:33)
31. "I _____ set my bow in the cloud" (Gen. 9:13)
33. "God. . .rested. . .from _____ his work" (Gen. 2:2)
34. "He careth _____ you" (1 Pet. 5:7)
36. Wind direction
37. Jacob's first wife (Gen. 29:23)
39. Saul's concubine (2 Sam. 21:11)
40. Esau's wife (Gen. 36:12)
41. "Why make ye this _____" (Mark 5:39)

43. "Let them be desolate. . .that say unto me, ____" (Ps. 40:15)
45. "This is the confidence that we have ____ him" (1 John 5:14)
46. Southern state, abbr.
48. Smallest state, abbr.

PUZZLE 5

by Kenda Turner

ACROSS

1. "Being justified freely by his grace through the _____ that is in Christ Jesus" (Rom. 3:24)
9. "I will sift the house of Israel. . . like as corn is sifted in a _____" (Amos 9:9)
10. Annoy
11. "Jesus said. . . 'If thou canst _____, all things are possible to him that believeth' " (Mark 9:23)
14. "I _____ no pleasant bread" (Dan. 10:3)
15. "_____ the knot" (get married)
16. 7, Rom. num.
18. "Man shall not _____ by bread alone" (Matt. 4:4)
19. Fervor
20. Delegate, abbr.
21. A swine
22. Jacob
26. Fifth letter of Hebrew alphabet
27. Fruit of the Spirit
28. Undergraduate degree
29. Southern state, abbr.
30. James and John, to Zebedee
31. One of two faithful spies sent to search Canaan
34. A preposition, meaning to the same degree
35. Biblical weed
37. Weird
39. What Boaz plucked off to signify redeeming Ruth
41. Southern continent, abbr.
42. Possessive pronoun
43. One of four seasons
44. Roman poet

46. Support group for alcoholics, abbr.
47. Sect of Jews during time of Christ

DOWN

1. "For _____ is as the sin of witchcraft" (1 Sam. 15:23)
2. The first woman
3. "Lead us not into temptation; but _____ us from evil" (Luke 11:4)
4. Come together
5. "_____ of knowledge of good and evil" (Gen. 2:9)
6. 2, Rom. num.
7. Mount of _____
8. Compass point
9. "_____ in awe, and sin not" (Ps. 4:4)
12. Active of watching
13. "He said, 'I am the voice of one crying in the _____' " (John 1:23)
17. Its capital is Des Moines, abbr.
21. "And the _____ of God, which passeth all understanding, shall keep your hearts and minds through Christ Jesus" (Phil. 4:7)
23. An orderly way of getting things done
24. Stomach muscle, for short
25. "And ye shall know the truth, and the truth shall make you _____" (John 8:32)
26. Exclamation of amusement
27. One of two faithful spies sent to search Canaan
30. What disrespectful children do
32. "Therefore shall a man _____ his father and his mother, and shall cleave unto his wife" (Gen. 2:24)

33. "And the Spirit and the _____ say, 'Come' " (Rev. 22:17)
36. Unusual
38. Pronoun
40. Suffix for a growth
41. International signal of distress
45. Opposite of out

PUZZLE 6

by John H. Thornberg

ACROSS

1. "Sacrifice. . .____ ____ of turtle-doves" (Luke 2:24) (2 words)
5. Bashful
7. "[David] feigned himself ____" (1 Sam. 21:13)
10. "Sword of the Spirit, . . .the ____ of God" (Eph. 6:17)
11. Also known as, abbr.
12. Information
13. "Ye do ____, not knowing the scriptures" (Matt. 22:29)
14. Triple Sugar Iron agar, abbr.
15. Male singing voice
16. Jewish scriptures
18. "Neither shall the cruse of ____ fail" (1 Kings 17:14)
19. "Be it unto ____ according to thy word" (Luke 1:38)
21. "____ unto them that call evil good" (Isa. 5:20)
22. "The staff of his ____ was like a weaver's beam" (1 Sam. 17:7)
24. "A thousand shall fall ____ thy side" (Ps. 91:7)
26. To fill with joy
28. "Though he slay me, ____ will I trust in him" (Job 13:15)
30. "____and feather him!"
32. "Sharper than any two-edged ____" (Heb. 4:12)
34. A beaver____
36. "Shut the doors, and ____ them" (Neh. 7:3)
38. Accomplish
40. "____weapon that is formed against thee" (Isa. 54:17)
42. Motion picture
44. "Cain. . .dwelt in the land of ____" (Gen. 4:16)
46. "Where two ____ three are gathered" (Matt. 18:20)
48. Flying mammal
49. Southern Israeli desert
51. Regulation decreed by a church council
53. Animal pelt
54. Motorized coach
56. "Soul of Jonathan was ____ with. . . David" (1 Sam. 18:1)
57. "Cast him into the bottomless ____" (Rev. 20:3)
58. "[Samson] ____not that the Lord was departed" (Judg. 16:20)
59. "The trees of the Lord are full of ____" (Ps. 104:16)
60. "Held in with ____ and bridle" (Ps. 32:9)
61. Trivial

DOWN

1. "Stand in ____, and sin not" (Ps. 4:4)
2. Nautical left side
3. "For the ____, that flieth by day" (Ps. 91:5)
4. A part of the psyche
5. Schuss
6. "He [the horse] saith among the trumpets, ____" (Job 39:25)
7. "What is ____, that thou art mindful of him?" (Ps. 8:4)
8. Elementary particle
9. Has courage
11. Cinder
12. "That he would not ____ to come" (Acts 9:38)
14. Chinese ounces
15. "____ them about thy neck" (Prov. 6:21)
17. "The loving hind and pleasant ____" (Prov. 5:19)

18. Musical drama
20. A large tub
22. A furnace
23. "Though they be____ like crimson" (Isa. 1:18)
25. Small flap
27. "Their laying ____was known of Saul" (Acts 9:24)
29. Light brown
31. Isaac's replacement on the altar
33. Restaurant
35. Unruly throng
37. Mechanical monster
39. Piece of timber
41. "Defence shall be the munitions of ____" (Isa. 33:16)
43. Mover's truck
45. Shortfall
47. A genus of frogs
49. "A tough ____ to crack"
50. "Pike's Peak or____!"
52. "____ in the bud"
53. "Men of war ____ for the battle" (1 Chron. 12:8)
55. A pig ____
57. 3.14, the ratio of a circle's circumference to its diameter
58. "____ beseech thee" (Ps. 80:14)

PUZZLE 7

by Evelyn M. Boyington

ACROSS

1. "Then ____ was wroth with the seer" (2 Chron. 16:10)
4. "I do ____ to day and to morrow" (Luke 13:32)
9. "Behold, the ____ of the Lord cometh" (Isa. 13:9)
12. "His brethren. . .Gilalai, Maai, ____ and Judah" (Neh. 12:36)
14. "Which are blackish by reason of the ____" (Job 6:16)
15. "____ shall be as gods" (Gen. 3:5)
16. Elliptical
17. Relatives
19. "Thou shalt be for ____ to the fire" (Ezek. 21:32)
20. Female reproductive organ, comb. form
21. "I will ____ the other bullock" (1 Kings 18:23)
23. "He hath ____ the dough" (Hos. 7:4)
26. "Gather a certain ____ every day" (Exod. 16:4)
27. Makes warm
28. Northeastern area of the U.S., abbr.
29. "This is ____ of the Hebrews' children" (Exod. 2:6)
30. "The black horses. . .go forth into the ____ country" (Zech. 6:6)
31. A poem
32. King of Bashan (1 Kings 4:19)
33. "All the ____ thereof shall be burned with the fire" (Mic. 1:7)
34. Mimicked
35. "I am like a ____" (Ps. 102:6)
37. Snow vehicles
38. "And ____ gave names to all cattle" (Gen. 2:20)
39. "____ was a tiller of the ground" (Gen. 4:2)
40. "O thou fairest among ____" (Song of Sol. 1:8)
42. "Set it upon a ____" (Num. 21:8)
43. On or about, abbr.
45. "And he smote them ____ and thigh" (Judg. 15:8)
46. "To the ____ of the glory of our Lord Jesus Christ" (2 Thess. 2:14)
49. Albert, Allen, and Alex, for short
50. "The magicians and astrologers that were in all his ____" (Dan. 1:20)
51. "As it was in the days of ____" (Luke 17:26)

DOWN

1. "Not willing that ____ should perish" (2 Pet. 3:9)
2. "____ this great sight" (Exod. 3:3)
3. Preposition
4. "The people did hide themselves in ____" (1 Sam. 13:6)
5. Single
6. Religion, abbr.
7. Electrical engineer, abbr.
8. "In the hand of him that ____ thee" (Ezek. 28:9)
9. "When they had ____" (John 21:15)
10. "The ____ of violence is in their hands" (Isa. 59:6)
11. Affirmative
13. "They brought down the king from the ____ of the Lord" (2 Kings 11:19)
18. Belonging to Una
19. Festival
20. Small flying insects
21. Sag
22. "The ____ of the mountains is his pasture" (Job 39:8)
23. "The name of the third ____-Happuch" (Job 42:14)

24. "On the seventh day God _____ his work" (Gen. 2:2)
25. "Repented not of their _____" (Rev. 16:11)
27. "Then _____ king of Gezer came up to help" (Josh. 10:33)
30. "They chose Stephen. . .and Philip, and Prochorus and _____" (Acts 6:5)
31. "His ears are _____ unto their prayers" (1 Pet. 3:12)
33. "_____ me under the shadow of thy wings" (Ps. 17:8)
34. "An _____ unto my mother's children" (Ps. 69:8)
36. "Give us of your oil: for our _____ are gone out" (Matt. 25:8)

37. "John also was baptizing in Aenon near to _____" (John 3:23)
39. "Their visage is blacker than a _____" (Lam. 4:8)
40. World Hockey Association, abbr.
41. "All the best of the _____, and all the best of the wine" (Num. 18:12)
42. Teacher-parent organization, abbr.
43. "One of the villages in the plain of _____" (Neh. 6:2)
44. "When she was past _____" (Heb. 11:11)
47. "God shall _____ with you" (Gen. 48:21)
48. "The Lord shut him _____" (Gen. 7:16)

by Sissy Magnusson

ACROSS

1. Our ____ is with the Father (1 John 1:3)
11. Constellation (Job 9:9)
12. The ____ chapter (1 Cor. 13)
13. Southern slang for poor
14. A populous place (Nah. 3:8)
15. Son of Peleth (Num. 16:1)
16. Printer's measure
17. To boast
20. Wonder
21. Vehicle (Amos 2:13)
23. An age
25. Otherwise
26. ____ me, expression of sorrow
27. Pure
30. Writing instrument
31. Forbidden insult (Matt. 5:22)
33. Great happiness
35. Montpelier's state, abbr.
36. Pertaining to wings
37. Astronomical unit, abbr.
38. Oldest son of Noah (Gen. 9:18)
40. Head nurse, abbr.
42. Sooner than
43. Oldest son of Adam (Gen. 4:1)
46. City on the coast of Caesarea (Josh. 11:2)
48. Short for Leonard
49. A riddle
51. None in Gilead? (Jer. 8:22)
53. Come in
55. Opposite of pride (1 Pet. 5:5)
56. Will come out of Jacob (Num. 24:17)

DOWN

1. Control of one's feelings (Eph. 4:2)
2. Son of Jose (Luke 3:28–29)
3. New York's largest island, abbr.
4. A fruit of the spirit "____-suffering" (Gal. 5:22)
5. Biblical city (1 Chron. 8:12)
6. "____ to anger" (Neh. 9:17)
7. Truthfulness
8. Intravenous, abbr.
9. The absence of strife
10. Satisfaction
13. Keep on keeping on
18. Kingly
19. Article
22. European mountain
24. Expression of satisfaction
27. Loving
28. Son of Zibeon (Gen. 36:24)
29. "Healthy" heart (Prov. 14:30)
32. Earthquake state, abbr.
34. In like manner
39. "____ of salvation" (Eph. 6:17)
41. Name meaning "wild goat" (Gen. 36:28)
44. Airman, abbr.
45. 2, Rom. num.
47. "To ____ is better than sacrifice" (1 Sam. 15:22)
50. Name meaning "my brother" (1 Chron. 5:15)
52. Lights, abbr.
54. Egyptian sun god

by Beverley Barnes

ACROSS

1. "Confession is made unto ____" (Rom. 10:10)
8. To make a choice
11. "There ____ I in the midst of them" (Matt. 18:20)
12. Woman's name
13. A narrow fold or wrinkle
15. "To know. . .the ____ of my days" (Ps. 39:4)
18. Man's title
19. North America, abbr.
20. "____ the day in which he was taken up" (Acts 1:2)
21. "____, Father" (Mark 14:36)
22. Southwestern state, abbr.
23. Playful aquatic mammal
25. The book before Nehemiah
26. Man's name
28. "Brightness of his ____" (Heb. 1:3)
29. New covenant writings, abbr.
31. "____, I say unto you" (John 3:3)
33. Suffix
34. A precious stone
35. Opposite of yes
36. Holds royal office
39. One of Paul's epistles, abbr.
41. Cable News Network, abbr.
42. Gym class, abbr.
44. Meaning partial or half, prefix
46. "Put thou my tears into thy ____" (Ps. 56:8)
49. Prince of Islam
50. First person contraction
51. "He shall ____ like a lion" (Hos. 11:10)
53. "The ____ of the valleys" (Song of Sol. 2:1)
54. "He gave his only ____ Son" (John 3:16)
55. Helena's state, abbr.

DOWN

1. "The Lord called ____: and he answered, Here am I" (1 Sam. 3:4)
2. The end of a prayer
3. "____ the fatherless and widows" (James 1:27)
4. Grown-up
5. Black sticky substance
6. Observation post, abbr.
7. The book after Leviticus
8. Short agreement
9. A long narrow triangular flag
10. A streetcar
14. Chief ____ Horse
16. "Day of ____" (Lev. 23:28)
17. "My God; ____will I seek thee" (Ps. 63:1)
24. A city of Judah (Josh. 15:39)
27. "____ evil with good" (Rom. 12:21)
30. "We have seen and do ____" (1 John 4:14)
32. Participle ending
33. The meek shall ____ the earth (Matt. 5:5)
37. Inward, prefix
38. South American language, abbr.
40. What David wrote
43. Plural of E
45. 1,000 x 1,000, abbr.
46. Put this on baby when feeding
47. Abram's nephew (Gen. 12:5)
48. Of every tree thou mayest ____ (Gen. 2:16)
52. Do, ____, mi

by Mary Louise DeMott

ACROSS

1. God sent this man a dream of a ladder with angels ascending and descending on it (Gen. 28:12–16)
6. God called this man, from a burning bush, to free Israel from Egyptian bondage (Exod. 3:1–12)
11. Full of cheerful good humor
12. Jesus called this man to follow Him (John 1:43)
14. Osmium, chem. symbol
15. Delirium tremens, abbr.
17. Manganese, chem. symbol
18. Maine, abbr.
19. Not existing before, recently made or invented
21. Belonging to the church's first missionary (Acts 9:15–16; 13:1–2)
24. Suitable or quick at learning
25. Tailless monkeys, or large uncouth men
27. Unwell
28. Without payment, costing nothing
29. His Highness, abbr.
30. Lanthanum, chem. symbol
32. Milliliter, abbr.
33. Rural route, abbr.
34. Jesus called this man to follow Him (John 1:44–51)
35. Society of Jesus, abbr.
37. Physical Education, abbr.
38. In the matter of, about, concerning, abbr.
39. Printer's unit of measure
41. Electrically charged particles
43. Fodder
45. A narrative or story
47. Life-support system, abbr.
48. Carried

50. Central Intelligence Agency, abbr.
51. Exclamation of satisfaction
52. Laughter sound
53. Eastern Time, abbr.
55. Rue, Amer. abbr.
56. Excellent, most impressive or splendid
59. Person who worked iron
61. God called this man to become Israel's first High Priest (Lev. 8:2)
62. God called this man to marry a harlot as a picture to Israel of their relationship with God (Hos. 1:1–4)

DOWN

1. Sold into salvery by his brothers (Gen. 37:27–28)
2. Authorized Version of the Bible, abbr.
3. Criminal Investigation Department of Scotland Yard, abbr.
4. Hardy cereal plants grown in cool climates
5. Barrel, abbr.
6. Military Policeman, abbr.
7. Units of electrical resistance
8. Breaking of religious or moral law
9. Elevated railway
10. An affected smile
11. God called this man to warn Nineveh about coming judgment unless it repented (Jon. 1:1–2)
13. Jesus called this fisherman to follow Him (Matt. 4:18–20)
16. The territory of a sultan
20. Us
22. Artificial Intelligence, abbr.
23. Lines, abbr.
24. Argon, chem. symbol
26. Strikes with open hand

28. Moving swiftly, nimble
31. Consumed
32. To damage, to spoil
35. This man was called to help Paul (Acts 15:40)
36. God called this man to lead Israel into Canaan (Josh. 1:1–9)
39. God called this man to be the successor to Elijah (1 Kings 19:16–17)
40. Fleshy or full of subject matter
42. Not specified, abbr.
43. "____, every one that thirsteth" (Isa. 55:1)
44. KJV you

46. Actinium, chem. symbol
48. Tropical plant with a tuberous root used for food
49. Item used for demonstration
52. Opposite of him
54. It is, poetic contraction
57. Ma's mate
58. Battalion, abbr.
59. Hush!
60. Tellurium, chem. symbol

by Malina D. English

ACROSS

1. Bottommost parts of faces
6. Having to do with either the North or South Poles
11. The sister of Tubal-cain (Gen. 4:22)
12. Lets up
14. Preposition
15. "The soldiers. . .____ his side" (John 19:34)
17. Military police, abbr.
18. Man's name
20. Not the clergy
21. 7, Rom. num.
22. Paul's original name
24. Root-mean-square, abbr.
25. One hundreth of a dollar
26. Motors
28. "The ____ of the wicked have robbed me" (Ps. 119:61)
29. "I will surely do thee ____" (Gen. 32:12)
30. Steal
31. Mix together
33. "The ____ of death are fallen upon me" (Ps. 55:4)
36. Rodents
37. Jesus is the ____ of man
38. Chocolate sandwich cookie
39. Article that precedes a vowel
40. "I have ____ ashes like bread" (Ps. 102:9)
42. Astronomical unit, abbr.
43. Selfish part of the psyche, according to Freud
44. "We were ____ of God to be put in trust with the gospel" (1 Thess. 2:4)
46. Physician, in other words, abbr.
47. "It is easier for a camel to go through the eye of a ____, than for a rich man to enter into the kingdom" (Mark 10:25)
49. Washes away
51. "The angel appeared to [Joseph] in a ____" (Matt. 1:20)
52. Person who gives something

DOWN

1. Biblical land
2. Expression of laughter or sarcasm
3. Mischievous child
4. "I will fasten him as a ____ in a sure place" (Isa. 22:23)
5. Cut
6. Agreements
7. "____ my voice, and I will be your God" (Jer. 7:23)
8. Boy
9. Preposition
10. Call to memory
11. "Make a joyful ____ unto God" (Ps. 66:1)
13. Expels saliva
16. Edges
19. Small chunk of gold
21. Seller
23. "Faith. . .stopped the mouths of ____" (Heb. 11:33)
25. Egyptian capital
27. Biblical land (Gen. 4:16)
28. Rod
30. Made fresh
31. Organ of thought
32. Alit
33. Dorothy's dog
34. Peruser of books
35. Turns acid
37. Melchizedek was king of this (Gen. 14:18)

40. Girl's name
41. Roman emperor
44. Lemon drink
45. Donald, for short
48. More, suffix
50. "____ thou that which is good"
    (2 Kings 10:5)

PUZZLE 12

by Linda Nunn

ACROSS

1. "Joshua the son of ____"
   (Deut. 34:9)
4. "And I sent the ____ before you"
   (Josh. 24:12)
9. "Blessed are ____" (Matt. 5:11)
11. One of the kings of Judah
    (1 Kings 15:11)
12. "He had compassion ____ him"
    (Luke 10:33)
13. "Intending after ____ to bring him
    forth to the people" (Acts 12:4)
15. "Thy father made our ____ griev-
    ous" (1 Kings 12:4)
16. "The ____ shall be first"
    (Matt. 19:30)
17. "____ burden is light"
    (Matt. 11:30)
18. "There was one ____, a prophet-
    ess" (Luke 2:36)
21. "And a certain woman named
    ____" (Acts 16:14)
24. "When I am weak, then am I
    ____" (2 Cor. 12:10)
25. "____ strong" (1 Sam. 4:9)
26. "I am that bread of ____"
    (John 6:48)
28. "As the apple ____"
    (Song of Sol. 2:3)
29. "What must I do to be ____?"
    (Acts 16:30)
31. "Better is it that thou shouldest not
    ____" (Eccles. 5:5)
34. "O generation of ____"
    (Matt. 3:7)
37. "And the glory of the Lord abode
    upon mount ____" (Exod. 24:16)
39. Seeds that can be made into soup
42. A natural substance containing a
    valuable metal
43. New Testament, abbr.

44. Latin that is, abbr.
45. "___ man can serve two masters"
    (Matt. 6:24)
46. "And whatsoever goeth upon his
    ____" (Lev. 11:27)
50. "He hath ____ great things"
    (Joel 2:20)
52. "There shall be weeping and ____
    of teeth" (Luke 13:28)
55. "Though they be ____ like crim-
    son, they shall be as wool"
    (Isa. 1:18)
56. "Rebekah. . .the daughter of
    Bethuel the ____"
    (Gen. 25:20)
57. "We remember the. . .____"
    (Num. 11:5)

DOWN

1. "I tell you, ____ " (Luke 13:3)
2. United Service Organizations,
   abbr.
3. "I was afraid, because I was ____"
   (Gen. 3:10)
4. "____, everyone that thirsteth"
   (Isa. 55:1)
5. "Believe ____, and she shall be
   made whole" (Luke 8:50)
6. "Birds of the air have ____"
   (Luke 9:58)
7. "Arise, Peter; slay and ____"
   (Acts 11:7)
8. Poet Elliot's initials
9. "Sing unto the Lord, O ____
   saints" (Ps. 30:4)
10. One of the sons of Judah
    (Gen. 46:12)
14. A male voice part
17. "And [Jesus] called, saying, ____,
    arise" (Luke 8:54)
18. "Thou ____ my King" (Ps. 44:4)
19. Compass direction, abbr.
20. "Rock of ____, cleft for me"
21. Pounds, abbr.

22. "_____, though I walk"
(Ps. 23:4)
23. French word for island
27. "I will fear no _____" (Ps. 23:4)
30. "I am the true _____"
(John 15:1)
32. "Who is worthy to _____ the
book?" (Rev. 5:2)
33. "So they two _____ until they came
to Bethlehem" (Ruth 1:19)
35. Right, abbr.
36. Yes, in Italian or Spanish
37. "Speaking to yourselves in psalms
and. . .spiritual _____" (Eph. 5:19)
38. Sarcasm

40. "Fine _____ is the righteousness of
saints" (Rev. 19:8)
41. "Some _____ fell by the way side"
(Matt. 13:4)
46. 23rd letter of the Greek alphabet
47. Expression of triumph
48. "That I may _____ Christ"
(Phil. 3:8)
49. Chemical symbol for tin
51. Spanish word for gold
53. "To the dwelling of _____"
(Num. 21:15)
54. "_____ ye therefore"
(Matt. 28:19)

Puzzle 13

by Janet Adkins

ACROSS

1. "[I] will ____ praise to the name of the Lord most high" (Ps. 7:17)
5. "Famine and pestilence shall ____ him" (Ezek. 7:15)
7. "He hath chosen Solomon my son to ____ upon the throne" (1 Chron. 28:5)
8. "When it shall turn to the LORD, the ____ shall be taken away" (2 Cor. 3:16)
10. Letter before dee
11. "____ is confounded and dismayed" (Jer. 48:1)
13. Self-addressed envelope, abbr.
14. Religious group
15. "There ____ him ten men that were lepers" (Luke 17:12)
17. "And hired counsellors against them to frustrate their ____" (Ezra 4:5)
19. "And if he trespass against thee ____ times in a day. . .forgive him" (Luke 17:4)
21. Plural ending
22. Belonging to Judah's first son (Gen. 38:2–3)
23. Prohibit
24. Alcoholics Anonymous, abbr.
25. Robinson Crusoe author
27. "They found him. . .sitting in the midst of the ____" (Luke 2:46)
29. "____ thy morsel in the vinegar" (Ruth 2:14)
30. "I will ____ in thy truth" (Ps. 86:11)
31. Amount, abbr.
32. Girl's name

34. Late general/president
35. Father of Ahira (Num. 1:15)
36. Saints, abbr.
37. Fur-bearing aquatic animals
39. Syringe, for short

DOWN

1. "I will ____ no wicked thing before mine eyes" (Ps. 101:3)
2. Method of administering medication, abbr.
3. "Not a ____, lest. . .he fall" (1 Tim. 3:6)
4. "That he was gone to be ____ with a man that is a sinner" (Luke 19:7)
5. Expire
6. Equip
7. "And Samuel answered Saul. . . 'I am the ____' " (1 Sam. 9:19)
9. "Gird yourselves, and ____, ye priests" (Joel 1:13)
10. "I have ____ you to be carried away captives" (Jer. 29:7)
11. "And there followed him a ____ of meat from the king" (2 Sam. 11:8)
12. Girl's name, for short
13. "Have they not ____?" (Judg. 5:30)
14. "For they were ____ afraid" (Mark 9:6)
16. "They did ____ ____ and ceased not" (Ps. 35:15) (2 words)
18. "Let my ____ go, that they may serve me" (Exod. 9:1)
19. "And the cup was found in Bejamin's ____" (Gen. 44:12)
20. Political cartoonist
23. Gaucho's weapon

26. "No grapes on the vine, nor figs on the _____ tree" (Jer. 8:13)
27. "All things which were _____ and goodly are departed" (Rev. 18:14)
28. "He was strong as the _____" (Amos 2:9)
30. "For the fierce _____ of the Lord is upon you" (2 Chron. 28:11)
33. "Let us meet. . .in the plain of _____" (Neh. 6:2)
34. Contraction
36. Theatre sign when there are no more seats, abbr.
38. European Plan, abbr.

by Elaine Okupski

ACROSS

1. "Do him no ____" (Jer. 39:12)
5. Abbott, Fr.
9. "Also I shook my ____"
   (Neh. 5:13)
12. Oil of ____, skin softener
13. "The ____ of the Lord is
    clean, enduring for ever"
    (Ps. 19:9)
14. "Do they not ____ that devise
    evil?" (Prov. 14:22)
15. Puts on
16. "And it is a ____ thing that the
    king requireth" (Dan. 2:11)
17. "Now as he walked by the ____ of
    Galilee" (Mark 1:16)
18. Father of Enos (Gen. 5:6)
19. "Blessed ____ the pure in heart"
    (Matt. 5:8)
20. "And ____ ye not, but pursue after
    your enemies" (Josh. 10:19)
21. One of the sons of Gad
    (Gen. 46:16)
23. Librarian's whisper
25. "Ye have ____ treasure together
    for the last days" (James 5:3)
28. "For ____ is the kingdom of heav-
    en" (Matt. 5:10)
32. "And it shall be unto them. . .that
    have sworn ____" (Ezek. 21:23)
33. Weird
34. Welcomes
36. "____, and be baptized every one
    of you" (Acts 2:38)
37. "He. . .chooseth a tree that will not
    ____" (Isa. 40:20)
38. "That which groweth of ____ own
    accord" (Lev. 25:5)
39. "I will bless the ____ at all times"
    (Ps. 34:1)
42. "Let us ____ with patience the
    race that is set before us"
    (Heb. 12:1)
44. "And I will give unto thee the
    ____ of the kingdom of heaven"
    (Matt. 16:19)
48. ____ Maria
49. Mongrels
50. "And the rest will ____ in order
    when I come" (1 Cor. 11:34)
    (2 words)
51. 22nd letter of alphabet
52. Swedish name
53. Nickname for Nathaniel
54. "Make thee an ____ of gopher
    wood" (Gen. 6:14)
55. "That the ____ men be sober,
    grave, temperate, sound in faith"
    (Titus 2:2)
56. "I will give thee. . .a ____ of
    apparel" (Judg. 17:10)

DOWN

1. Bricklayers' troughs
2. "Burn plant"
3. To speak vehemently
4. "The Lord is ____ ____"
   (Ps. 23:1) (2 words)
5. "They fell on their face, and were
   sore ____" (Matt. 17:6)
6. "____ ye one another's burdens"
   (Gal. 6:2)
7. "Because thou ____ the ark
   of the Lord GOD" (1 Kings 2:26)
8. "And ____ the lamp of God went
   out in the temple of the Lord"
   (1 Sam. 3:3)
9. "Neither shall ye touch it, ____ ye
   die" (Gen. 3:3)
10. Length times width
11. "____ without ceasing"
    (1 Thess. 5:17)

20. "They wandered about in ____ and goatskins" (Heb. 11:37)
22. "Return unto thy ____ my soul" (Ps. 116:7) (2 words)
24. "A great ____, knit at the four corners" (Acts 10:11)
25. Domesticated swine
26. "That which ye have spoken in the ____" (Luke 12:3)
27. "I ____ no pleasant bread" (Dan. 10:3)
29. Anger
30. ____-tin-tin, hero dog
31. "And God ____ them in the firmament of the heaven" (Gen. 1:17)

35. Put beads on a string
36. "It shall be both scoured, and ____ in water" (Lev. 6:28)
39. Molten rock
40. "Stretch forth thine hand with thy rod ____ the streams" (Exod. 8:5)
41. To stink
43. "The Pharisees began to ____ him vehemently" (Luke 11:53)
45. Jacob's brother (Gen. 25:26)
46. Abominable snowman
47. Editor's instruction
49. Government agency

by Michael J. Landi

ACROSS

1. "Away with such a fellow from the earth, for it is not ____ that he should live" (Acts 22:22)
4. "The joy of thy ____" (Matt. 25:21)
7. "Do thyself no ____" (Acts 16:28)
9. "A feast of wines on the ____" (Isa. 25:6)
11. "Believe also in ____" (John 14:1)
12. "And sow wickedness, ____ the same" (Job 4:8)
13. "Called to be ____ apostle" (1 Cor. 1:1)
14. A son of Benjamin (Gen. 46:21)
17. "Seeing he giveth to all ____" (Acts 17:25)
18. "Chains had been plucked asunder by him, and the fetters broken in pieces: neither could any man ____ him" (Mark 5:4)
19. "His life a ____ for many" (Matt. 20:28)
22. "Hath the ____ of the Lord been revealed?" (John 12:38)
25. "Because Judas had the ____, that Jesus had said unto him" (John 13:29)
26. "____, and do thou likewise" (Luke 10:37)
27. "Wash his feet with ____" (Luke 7:38)
28. "And stamp with thy foot, and say, ____ for all the evil abominations of the house of Israel!" (Ezek. 6:11)
29. "That where I am, there ye may ____" (John 14:3)
30. "Let him ____ the death" (Matt. 15:4)
32. "Whose shoes I am not worthy to ____" (Matt. 3:11)
34. "Be ye not as the horse, ____ as the mule" (Ps. 32:9)
35. "Do ye not therefore ____, because ye know not the scriptures?" (Mark 12:24)
36. "I ____ in Sion a chief corner stone" (1 Pet. 2:6)
38. Blew trumpet before ark of God (1 Chron. 15:24)
40. Preposition
41. Forefather of Jesus, El-mo-dam was the son of him (Luke 3:28)
42. "Simon ____ -Jona" (Matt. 16:17)
43. 11th letter of Hebrew alphabet

DOWN

1. "His eyes were as a ____ of fire" (Rev. 19:12)
2. Same as, or that is, Lat. abbr.
3. "Thou shalt not ____ the Lord thy God" (Matt. 4:7)
5. "Whose ____ have I taken?" (1 Sam. 12:3)
6. "Mighty in ____ and word" (Luke 24:19)
7. "That they should seek the Lord, if ____ they might feel after him" (Acts 17:27)
8. "Is not ____ to give" (Mark 10:40)
10. "Who shall ____ us from the love of Christ?" (Rom. 8:35)
13. "But having seen them ____ off" (Heb. 11:13)
15. "Whose is this ____ and superscription?" (Matt. 22:20)

16. "Honour all _____ " (1 Pet. 2:17)
20. "The pen of the ___ is in vain" (Jer. 8:8)
21. First Gospel, abbr.
22. "Believe ye that I am _____ to do this?" (Matt. 9:28)
23. "Thou shalt forget thy _____" (Job 11:16)
24. "And being in an _____ he prayed more earnestly" (Luke 22:44)
28. "The prince of the power of the _____" (Eph. 2:2)
29. "To _____ I am ashamed" (Luke 16:3)

30. Gold coin used in Palestine (Ezra 2:69 RSV & ASV)
31. "The troops of _____ looked, the companies of Sheba waited for them" (Job 6:19)
33. Period of time
34. "Neither by any other _____" (James 5:12)
36. "Lot is cast into the _____" (Prov. 16:33)
37. Greek, abbr.
38. Hebrew 5th month
39. "Pass over through _____, the coast of Moab" (Deut. 2:18)

PUZZLE 16

by John Thornberg

ACROSS

1. "Whose ____ is in his hand"
   (Matt. 3:12)
4. To sink downward
7. "Turn not ____ from following
   the Lord" (1 Sam. 12:20)
9. Half quarts
12. Where David's story begins
    (2 words)
14. Nothing
15. Doze
17. Raw material
18. "Queen of ____" (1 Kings 10:1)
20. "____ the kine to the cart"
    (1 Sam. 6:7)
21. "Cast him into the ____ of lions"
    (Dan. 6:16)
22. Deoxyribonucleic acid, abbr.
23. "Under a pomegranate ____"
    (1 Sam. 14:2)
24. "Sing unto the Lord ____ ____
    song" (Isa. 42:10) (2 words)
25. Prohibit
28. ____ and flow
31. A friend, Fr.
32. Former
33. Sheltered side
34. Marker
35. "As the ____ ran, he shot an
    arrow" (1 Sam. 20:36)
36. David was one, in other words
43. Fixed gaze
44. "Jonah was exceeding glad of the
    ____" (Jon. 4:6)
45. Light brown
46. "____ no man any thing"
    (Rom. 13:8)

DOWN

1. "Instruments made of ____"
   (2 Sam. 6:5)
2. Advertisements, abbr.
3. "Cast the ____ on the right side"
   (John 21:6)
4. A mineral spring
5. Point at target
6. Wildebeest
7. "____ ____ shall devour before
   him" (Ps. 50:3) (2 words)
8. A Christmas carol (2 words)
10. One who lives in a tent
11. "Worthy is the Lamb that was
    ____" (Rev. 5:12)
13. "A rod out of the ____ of Jesse"
    (Isa. 11:1)
14. Affirmative expression
16. A legume
18. "A deep ____ fell on Abram"
    (Gen. 15:12)
19. "____ the son of Ner"
    (2 Sam. 2:8)
25. A baseball ____
26. Gather great numbers
27. "Jonah was in the belly of the
    ____" (Jon. 1:17)
29. "His spittle [fell] down upon his
    ____" (1 Sam. 21:13)
30. "David arose from off his ____"
    (2 Sam. 11:2)
37. "[David] did ____ the shew-
    bread" (Matt. 12:4)
38. An epoch
39. "The ____ of a ready writer"
    (Ps. 45:1)
40. The conscious self
41. "Frankincense upon each ____"
    (Lev. 24:7)
42. "A word spoken in ____ season"
    (Prov. 15:23)

by Mary Louise DeMott

ACROSS

1. Father of 23 and 48 Across (Gen. 4:21)
4. Father of those who dwell in tents (Gen. 4:20)
8. A tract of open grassland
10. Pursuing wild animals for food
13. A length measured in yards
16. To rub or scrape out
17. Serial, abbr.
18. Suitable
20. Iridium, chem. symbol
21. Dry cut stalks of grain
23. Musical instrument with strings stretched on a roughly triangular frame
24. Barium, chem. symbol
26. Fermented grape juice
28. No
30. Using land to grow crops
33. Color of the sky
35. First note of the musical scale
36. Argon, chem. symbol
37. "____ the mighty hunter" (Gen. 10:8–9)
40. A bag, or envelope, inflated with air
41. Rural Electrification Administration, abbr.
42. Einsteinium, chem. symbol
43. Mystery writer Christie's first name
46. Latin, Locus Sigilli, means place of the seal, abbr.
47. School, abbr.
48. Musical instrument made of pipes, that air is forced through

DOWN

1. A summer month
2. A person who carries something
3. Unit of money in Turkey
4. A summer month
5. Thorny or prickly plant with woody stem
6. Forward section of lowest balcony
7. Tending a flock of sheep
9. Opposite of west
11. Walk or run with quick, light steps
12. Not specified, abbr.
14. To pull back his hunting equipment for 37 Across
15. Gallium, chem. symbol
19. Tantalum, chem. symbol
21. Number 39 Down turns this when he works
22. Opposite of husband
24. Bachelor of Arts, abbr.
25. Opposite of 28 Across
27. Sodium, chem. symbol
28. National Guard, abbr.
29. Fluid, abbr.
31. Mother
32. Noncommissioned Officer, abbr.
34. Mottled yellow and green citrus fruits
36. Father of 7 Down (Gen. 4:2)
37. Built the ark, the father of zoology (Gen. 6:13–14)
38. To pull something with difficulty
39. Father of 30 Across
44. Preposition
45. Home run, abbr.

PUZZLE 18

by Joyce Handzo

ACROSS

1. "Rule them with a ____ of iron" (Rev. 2:27)
3. "At the ____ of Jesus every knee should bow" (Phil. 2:10)
6. A bitter compound used in drugs and dyes
10. Utah, abbr.
11. "The ____ fell upon Jonah" (Jon. 1:7)
12. To regard with affection
14. Rhode Island, abbr.
15. "Go thee one way ___ other" (Ezek. 21:16)
17. "____ thy mouth wide" (Ps. 81:10)
18. For example, Lat. abbr.
20. "The days that Adam lived were ____ hundred and thirty" (Gen. 5:5)
21. Street, abbr.
23. "Jesus died and ____ again" (1 Thess. 4:14)
24. One who selects the contents of a publication
27. Associate in Applied Science, abbr.
29. Officer of the British Empire, abbr.
30. "Women ____ themselves in modest apparel" (1 Tim. 2:9)
32. "We are not ____ to answer thee" (Dan. 3:16)
35. Ribonucleic acid, abbr.
36. "They ____ unto it a lace of blue" (Exod. 39:31)
37. Northeast, abbr.
38. "The angels of God ____ him" (Gen. 32:1)
39. "____ that man" (2 Thess. 3:14)
41. Social Security, abbr.
42. Metal containers
44. "And the ____ stood still" (Josh. 10:13)
46. "The coat was without ____" (John 19:23)
48. Anno Domini, abbr.
50. "For God ____ loved the world" (John 3:16)
52. "Ye do ____, not knowing the scriptures" (Matt. 22:29)
54. "All the fiery ____ of the wicked" (Eph. 6:16)
56. "His ____ went to Jerusalem every year" (Luke 2:41)
57. "The ____ of all flesh is come before me" (Gen. 6:13)

DOWN

1. "Thou shalt not speak evil of the ____ of thy people" (Acts 23:5)
2. Old Testament, abbr.
3. "There is none righteous, ____, not one" (Rom. 3:10)
4. Makes amends for sin
5. Each, abbr.
6. Ampere, abbr.
7. "A faithful witness will not ____" (Prov. 14:5)
8. Vessels used to make tea or coffee
9. Maine, abbr.
11. Measurement in only one direction
13. "Gamaliel, a ____ of the law" (Acts 5:34)
16. "In the first chariot were ____ horses" (Zech. 6:2)
19. "Surely ____ and mercy shall follow me" (Ps. 23:6)
22. "Write them upon the ____ of thine heart" (Prov. 7:3)
25. Very fat

26. Referee, abbr.
28. "Go to the _____, thou sluggard" (Prov. 6:6)
30. "He took them up in his _____" (Mark 10:16)
31. A cereal plant
32. "Take up the _____ out of the burning" (Num. 16:37)
33. "Why make ye this _____, and weep?" (Mark 5:39)
34. "The lord commended the _____ steward" (Luke 16:8)
40. "Their _____ hath been to feed cattle" (Gen. 46:32)
42. California, abbr.

43. "These things saith the _____" (Rev. 3:14)
45. "Canst thou put a hook into his _____?" (Job 41:2)
47. "Give _____, O Lord, unto my prayer" (Ps. 86:6)
49. "_____ shall judge his people" (Gen. 49:16)
51. General Practitioner, abbr.
53. Right, abbr.
55. Road, abbr.

PUZZLE 19

by Linda Nunn

ACROSS

1. "Like the roaring of the ____" (Isa. 5:30)
4. "For ____ thou art" (Gen. 3:19)
8. "The ____ shall live by faith" (Rom. 1:17)
12. "There was no room for them in the ____" (Luke 2:7)
13. "They called his name ____" (Gen. 25:25)
14. "And the rain was ____ the earth forty days and forty nights" (Gen. 7:12)
15. A desert region of south Israel
17. Virtual Reality, abbr.
18. New Testament, abbr.
19. "And the king loved ____ above all the women" (Esther 2:17)
20. "I have given ____ unto the children of Lot for a possession" (Deut. 2:9)
22. "We have sent therefore Judas and ____ " (Acts 15:27)
24. "And will ____ their land" (2 Chron. 7:14)
27. Just ____ ____ Am, hymn title (2 words)
28. "But if ye ____ and devour one another" (Gal. 5:15)
31. As easy as ____
32. God's name for Himself: I ____ (Rom. 1:17)
33. "The wicked is ____ in the work of his own hands" (Ps. 9:16)
35. A historical period
37. "The ____ women, likewise, that they be in behavior as becometh holiness" (Titus 2:2)
38. Chemical symbol for tin
39. "And she named the child Ichabod, saying, The ____ is departed from Israel" (1 Sam. 4:21)
42. "O come, ____ us sing unto the Lord" (Ps. 95:1)
43. "And they slew the kings of Midian, beside the rest of them that were slain;. . .____ . . ." (Num. 31:8)

DOWN

1. "Whatsoever is not of faith is ____" (Rom. 14:23)
2. Compass direction, abbr.
3. "Some have entertained ____ unawares" (Heb. 13:2)
4. "Forgive us our ____ " (Matt. 6:12)
5. "The Lord seeth ____ not" (Ezek. 8:12)
6. "The same shall ____ it" (Mark 8:35)
7. Having turrets
8. "And ____ did evil in the sight of the Lord" (1 Kings 14:22)
9. "He was parted from them, and carried ____ into heaven" (Luke 24:51)
10. "Joshua the ____ of Nun was full of the spirit of wisdom" (Deut. 34:9)
11. An explosive
16. "For this is he that was spoken of by the prophet ____" (Matt. 3:3)
21. "____ ye for the kingdom of heaven is at hand" (Matt. 3:2)
23. "Jesus saith unto them ____ ____ he" (John 18:5) (2 words)
25. "Behold the fowls of the ____" (Matt. 6:26)
26. "Will thou break a ____ driven to and fro?" (Job 13:25)

45. Reverend, abbr.
46. Article
48. "Come unto me, all ____ that labor " (Matt. 11:28)
49. Cast a ballot
52. World War II day of triumph celebrated May 8, 1945
53. "Therefore say thou unto them, Thus saith the Lord of hosts; Turn ye unto ____ " (Zech. 1:3)
54. "Thou shalt therefore ____ this ordinance in his season from year to year" (Exod. 13:10)
56. "There was a ____ round about the throne " (Rev. 4:3)
59. "Now if ye be ready that at what time ye hear the sound of the. . . ____ " (Dan. 3:15)
60. Most, suffix

28. "For some of them thought, because Judas had the ____ " (John 13:29)
29. Anger, wrath
30. "And the children of Reuben and the children of Gad called the altar ____ " (Josh. 22:34)
32. "Be ye ____, and sin not" (Eph. 4:26)
34. "But let your communication be, Yea, yea; ____ " (Matt. 5:37)
36. "Behold, we count them happy which endure. Ye have heard of the patience of ____ " (James 5:11)
38. "And there came one of the ____ angels" (Rev. 17:1)
40. "We remember. . .the ____, and the onions, and the garlick" (Num. 11:5)
41. French composer

42. "And he shall purify the sons of ____ " (Mal. 3:3)
44. And, Lat.
46. "The words of ____, who was among the herdmen of Tekoa" (Amos 1:1)
47. Mr. Gingrich
50. To choose
51. "It is a people that do ____ in their heart" (Ps. 95:10)
55. Each, abbr.
57. ____ me, expression of sorrow
58. "Then will the Lord ____ jealous for his land, and pity his people" (Joel 2:18)

by Janet Kennedy

ACROSS

1. "With trumpets and sound of ____ make a joyful noise before the Lord, the King" (Ps. 98:6)
7. "The people piped with ____, and rejoiced" (1 Kings 1:40)
11. Able to give way
13. "And the fish of the ____" (Ps. 8:8)
14. Motor torpedo boat, abbr.
15. "David took an ____, and played with his hand: so Saul was refreshed" (1 Sam. 16:23)
16. "Praise him with stringed instruments and ____" (Ps. 150:4)
18. 51, Rom. num.
19. Fourth tone of the music scale
21. Lincoln's state, abbr.
22. Tellurium, chem. symbol
23. "That at what time ye hear the sound of the cornet, ____, harp" (Dan. 3:5)
26. "Ye ____ the light of the world" (Matt. 5:14)
29. First day of the week, abbr.
31. Black sticky substance
32. "That at the sound of the cornet, flute, harp, ____, psaltery" (Dan. 3:5)
35. "That chant to the sound of the ____" (Amos 6:5)
36. Gold, chem. symbol
37. Suffix: more
38. Kind of molding
39. "And the seven angels which had the seven ____ prepared themselves to sound" (Rev. 8:6)
42. Maritime province, abbr.
43. Inches per second, abbr.
44. Contraction of it was, poetic
45. "I ____ the way, the truth, the life" (John 14:6)
47. French article
48. "Come unto ____, all ye that labour and are heavy laden" (Matt. 11:28)
49. Miriam took one of these instruments (Exod. 15:20)
50. "For we have seen his ____ in the east, and are come to worship him" (Matt. 2:2)

DOWN

1. "Praise him upon the loud ____: praise him upon the high sounding ____" (Ps. 150:5)
2. Office of International Trade, abbr.
3. A blunt rejection
4. U.S. National League (baseball), abbr.
5. Suffix: forms the past tense of many words
6. "And the harp, and the viol, the ____, . . .are in their feasts" (Isa. 5:12)
7. Gym class, abbr.
8. "Thanksgivings. . .with singing, with cymbals, ____ and with harps" (Neh. 12:27)
9. Weird
10. "The trees of the Lord are full of ____" (Ps. 104:16)
12. "Give thee seed of this woman for the ____ which is lent to the Lord" (1 Sam. 2:20)
17. Opposite of untidy
20. Man's name
24. Messy
25. A large Australian bird similar to an ostrich

27. "No lion. . .nor any _____ beast shall go up thereon" (Isa. 35:9)

28. "That at that time ye hear the sound of the cornet, flute, . . . psaltery, _____, and all kinds of music, ye fall down" (Dan. 3:5)

30. "Nor to _____ authority over the man" (1 Tim. 2:12)

33. Witch's concoction

34. Throws

36. Not straight

40. "Come now, and let _____ reason together, saith the Lord" (Isa. 1:18)

41. High stature

45. American Medical Association, abbr.

46. Same source, Lat. abbr.

PUZZLE 21

by Michael Landi

ACROSS

1. Enemy (Luke 12:58)
7. "He is a ____ creature" (2 Cor. 5:17)
10. "He turned the ____ into dry land" (Ps. 66:6)
11. "Upon ____ stone shall be seven eyes" (Zech. 3:9)
12. Meaning abundant flow of water; John was baptizing near there (John 3:23)
14. "____ us not into temptation" (Matt. 6:13)
15. "Woe unto you, Pharisees! For ye tithe mint and ____" (Luke 11:42)
16. "It shall ____ given him" (James 1:5)
17. God cannot live in its presence (Isa. 59:2)
18. "And ____ the sacrifices of the dead" (Ps. 106:28)
19. "The race that is ____ before us" (Heb. 12:1)
20. "The kingdom of heaven is like unto a ____, that was cast into the sea" (Matt. 13:47)
21. "____ his feet in the blood of the wicked" (Ps. 58:10)
23. "Light of the body is the ____" (Luke 11:34)
27. Collection of 27 books, abbr.
28. "Felling a ____, the axe head fell into the water" (2 Kings 6:5)
29. The only son of Abraham by Sarah (Gen. 17:17–19)
32. The coarse and broken part of flax ready for spinning (Judg. 16:9)
33. "I the Lord search the heart, I ____ the reins" (Jer. 17:10)
34. "Of the ____ of Benjamin" (Phil. 3:5)
37. Place in the land of the Chaldees (Neh. 9:7)
38. "Shall be as an oak whose ____ fadeth" (Isa. 1:30)
40. "The ____ of the disciples was multiplied" (Acts 6:1)
42. "Your eyes shall see, and ____ shall say" (Mal. 1:5)
43. "And ____ about the paps with a golden girdle" (Rev. 1:13)
44. "Breastplates of fire, and of ____" (Rev. 21:20)

DOWN

1. "The ____ saw the angel of the Lord" (Num. 22:23)
2. Famine (Acts 11:28)
3. "Ye are of more ____ than many sparrows" (Matt. 10:31)
4. "They offered a ____ of the flock" (Ezra 10:19)
5. "Said unto her, What ____ thee, Hagar?" (Gen. 21:17)
6. "Went to Jerusalem every ____ at the feast of the passover" (Luke 2:41)
7. "The multitude of ____" (Jer. 46:25)
8. Hostility, hatred (Luke 23:12)
9. "Therefore ____ conclude that a man is justified by faith" (Rom. 3:28)
13. That is, Lat. abbr.
16. "Bring forth the ____ robe" (Luke 15:22)
17. "If any man among you ____ to be religious" (James 1:26)
19. Make holy (Eph. 5:26)

22. Temporary dwelling (2 Kings 7:8)
24. Another name for "bishop" (1 Tim. 5:1)
25. "Fall into a ____ on the sabbath day" (Matt. 12:11)
26. "The earth ____, and trembled" (Ps. 97:4)
30. "Lusts, which war against the ____" (1 Pet. 2:11)
31. Religious ode (Matt. 26:30)
35. Literally means "master;" title given by Jews to teachers of their law (John 1:38)
36. "I hate robbery for ____ offering" (Isa. 61:8)
39. "And smote off his ____" (Matt. 26:51)
41. Example, Lat. abbr.

PUZZLE 22

by Beverly Barnes

ACROSS

1. "The ____ is unto you, and to your children" (Acts 2:39)
8. "____ loves me, this I know"
12. "____ and perfume rejoice the heart" (Prov. 27:9)
14. Mississippi's neighbor, abbr.
15. "____ unto you, scribes and Pharisees, hypocrites!" (Matt. 23:25)
16. "When they had. . .gone six ____, he sacrificed oxen" (2 Sam. 6:13)
18. Personal smell, in other words, for short
19. Extra-terrestrials, abbr.
20. Central state, abbr.
21. Craggy hill
22. "____ and outs"
24. "Forsake me not ____" (Ps. 119:8)
25. The book between Joel and Obadiah
26. Garment belted at the waist
28. "____ Shaddai"
29. Single
31. Bachelor of Education degrees, abbr.
32. "The Spirit and the ____ say, Come" (Rev. 22:17)
34. Beverly, for short
35. Road, abbr.
36. "____ your enemies" (Matt. 5:44)
37. Compass point
38. Charges
40. Birds build these
44. Need this to solve a mystery
46. Compass point
48. Vowels: ____, ____, ____, o, u and sometimes y

50. Bends
52. Pluck guitar strings
54. Doctor of Divinity, abbr.
55. "Ye are not your ____" (1 Cor. 6:19)
56. "One of the least of ____" (Matt. 25:40)

DOWN

1. "Not in word, but in ____" (1 Cor. 4:20)
2. Violent uprising
3. A faithful and beloved brother (Col. 4:9)
4. ____ Sinai, abbr.
5. "With God nothing shall be ____" (Luke 1:37)
6. "Even the wind and the ____ obey him" (Mark 4:41)
7. Enclosure, abbr.
9. Spanish article
10. Southern continent, abbr.
11. "I love to tell the ____ of Jesus and His love"
13. "Aquila. . .with his wife Priscilla. . .were ____-makers" (Acts 18:2–3)
17. "Make you perfect, stablish, strengthen, ____ you" (1 Pet. 5:10)
18. "In whom we have ____ and access with confidence" (Eph. 3:12)
21. Transmit/receive, abbr.
23. Not, prefix
24. Biblical land: ____ of the Chaldees
25. Having, suffix
27. Jesus died on the ____
28. Garden of ____
29. Pregnancy doctor, abbr.
30. The first woman

31. The Israelites needed straw to make this (Exod. 5:7)
33. 4, Rom. num.
38. Money supply
39. Mouse's noise
41. "As far as the _____ is from the west" (Ps. 103:12)
42. A son of Adam (Luke 3:38)
43. The wheel of a car
45. The top of a jar
47. Earn
49. American English, abbr.
51. Therefore
53. "Unto every one of _____ is given grace" (Eph. 4:7)

PUZZLE 23

by Diana N. Rowland

ACROSS

1. "That the Lord spake unto ____ the son of Nun" (Josh. 1:1)
6. "____ and her towns, and the inhabitants" (Josh. 17:11)
11. "And Hur begat ____" (1 Chron. 2:20)
12. "Behold, this ____ shall be a witness" (Josh. 24:27)
14. "Jephunneh, and Pispah, and ____" (1 Chron. 7:38)
15. "____ thyself now with majesty" (Job 40:10)
17. "____ and all that are with her in the house" (Josh. 6:17)
18. "And it ____ worms" (Exod. 16:20)
19. "Whether they will ____ the way of the Lord" (Judg. 2:22)
21. "Gideon said, ____, O Lord GOD!" (Judg. 6:22)
23. "The children of Gad called the altar ____" (Josh. 22:34)
25. "Oliveyards which ye ____ not" (Josh. 24:13)
27. Preposition
28. "Shalt not give unto his ____, nor his daughter shalt thou ____" (Deut. 7:3) (2 words)
30. "As the ____, and all that came to hand" (Judg. 20:48)
32. Preposition
33. "Behold, the silver is with ____" (Judg. 17:2)
34. Bachelor of Arts degree, abbr.
35. Common nickname for a soldier
36. "Paul and Silas by night unto ____" (Acts 17:10)
38. "When I therefore was thus ____, did ____ use lightness?" (2 Cor. 1:17) (2 words)
41. Nickname for Edward
42. "Else if ye do in ____ wise go back" (Josh. 23:12)
44. "And upon the great ____ of his right foot" (Lev. 8:23)
45. "Judah took a wife for ____ his firstborn" (Gen. 38:6)

46. "It shall be that, ____ I ____, so shall ye do" (Judg. 7:17) (2 words)
47. "Tappuah, and ____" (Josh. 15:34)
49. ____, cosine, tangent
51. "And they burnt the city with ____" (Josh. 6:24)
53. "And ____ the kine to the cart" (1 Sam. 6:7)
54. "Go in this thy ____" (Judg. 6:14)
56. "Go and ____ in wait in the vineyards" (Judg. 21:20)
57. "He sat him down in a ____ of the city" (Judg. 19:15)
58. "Shelemiah the son of ____" (Jer. 36:26)

DOWN

1. "Nevertheless the Lord raised up ____" (Judg. 2:16)
2. Source of metals in the earth
3. "Behold, thy father is ____" (Gen. 48:1)
4. "All that thou commandest ____ we will do" (Josh. 1:16)
5. "Beat ____ the door, and ____ to the master" (Judg. 19:22) (2 words)
6. "____ that they ____ with the blood" (1 Sam. 14:33) (2 words)
7. "They ____ come to search out all the country" (Josh. 2:3)
8. "Proclaim in the ____ of the people" (Judg. 7:3)
9. "We ____ thy servants" (Josh. 9:8)
10. "Thou ____ him to have dominion" (Ps. 8:6)
13. "____ my Lord, if the Lord be with us" (Judg. 6:13)
16. "The Lord hath ____ me alive" (Josh. 14:10)
18. "Joshua did unto them as the Lord ____ him" (Josh. 11:9)
20. "There is ____ ____ all her multitude" (Ezek. 32:24) (2 words)
22. "From the wilderness and this ____ even unto the great river" (Josh. 1:4)
24. "She ____ upon the Assyrians her neighbours" (Ezek. 23:12)

26. Compass point, abbr.
27. "And they turned _____ thither" (Judg. 19:15)
29. "I will not fail thee, _____ forsake thee" (Josh. 1:5)
31. "I am old and stricken in _____" (Josh. 23:2)
34. "At the last it _____ like _____ serpent" (Prov. 23:32) (2 words)
36. "He is like the _____ that perish" (Ps. 49:12)
37. "Trode them down with _____" (Judg. 20:43)
39. "Thou shalt not curse the _____" (Lev. 19:14)
40. "And Rekem, and _____, and Taralah" (Josh. 18:27)

43. "The Lord your God giveth _____ to possess _____" (Josh. 1:11) (2 words)
46. "Brother of Eshcol, and brother of _____" (Gen. 14:13)
48. "Whosoever shall compel thee to go a _____, go with him twain" (Matt. 5:41)
50. "For _____ will give _____ into thine hand" (Josh. 8:18) (2 words)
52. "But the wheat and the _____ were not smitten" (Exod. 9:32)
54. "Hearken unto _____, ye men of Shechem" (Judg. 9:7)
55. Tuberculosis, abbr.

PUZZLE 24

by Michael J. Landi

ACROSS

1. Sister of David
   (1 Chron. 2:15–16)
7. "Unto ten virgins which took their
   ____" (Matt. 25:1)
10. City of Asher (Josh. 19:30)
12. "The ____ of the Lord"
    (Prov. 9:10)
14. "So let it be" (Matt. 6:13)
16. "____ no man any thing"
    (Matt. 13:8)
18. Acted as both judge and high
    priest in Israel (1 Sam. 1:9)
19. "____, but regarded as imposters"
    (2 Cor. 6:8 NIV)
20. A priest who returned from
    Babylon to Jerusalem with
    Zerubbabel (Neh. 12:1)
22. David's book, abbr.
23. Physician, abbr.
26. "____ their swords into plow-
    shares" (Isa. 2:4)
28. "For ____ to the faith among
    all nations, for his name"
    (Rom. 1:5)
30. Loyal member of David's court
    (1 Kings 1:8)
31. "He threw him into the ____"
    (Rev. 20:3 NIV)
33. Last book of the Bible, abbr.
34. "Upon the tip of the right ____ of
    Aaron" (Exod. 29:20)
37. "Yet have I set my ____ upon my
    holy hill" (Ps. 2:6)
39. "Turned about with a very small
    ____, whithersoever the governor
    listeth" (James 3:4)
40. Light of the body (Matt. 6:22)
41. Associate in Arts, abbr.
42. "Thou shalt not muzzle the ____"
    (Deut. 25:4)
43. "____ block" (Rom. 14:13)

DOWN

2. "If they have called the master of
   the house ____" (Matt. 10:25)
3. When King Ahaziah fled from
   Judah he went here
   (2 Kings 9:27)
4. "I ____ Alpha and Omega"
   (Rev. 1:8)
5. "Thou, O king, sawest, and
   behold a great ____" (Dan. 2:31)
6. "Then shall the ____ man leap as
   an hart" (Isa. 35:6)
8. "The sun and the ____ and the
   eleven stars" (Gen. 37:9)
9. "I was blind, now I ____"
   (John 9:25)
11. Son of Zephaniah (Zech. 6:14)
12. "Every prostitute receives a
    ____" (Ezek. 16:33 NIV)
13. "Not as one that beateth the
    ____" (1 Cor. 9:26)
15. "More in ____ than the sand"
    (Ps. 139:18)
17. "Peter went out, and ____"
    (Luke 22:62)
21. "Shall not ____ unto the word"
    (Deut. 4:2)
24. "A second, like to a bear, and it
    raised up itself on one side, and it
    had three ____ in the mouth of
    it" (Dan. 7:5)
25. "They will lick dust like a ____"
    (Mic. 7:17 NIV)
27. Firstborn of Hiel (1 Kings 16:34)
29. Son of Alphaeus (Mark 2:14)
31. "Satan himself is transformed
    into an ____" (2 Cor. 11:14)

32. "Thy father made our _____ grievous" (1 Kings 12:4)
35. Son of Omri and seventh king of the northern kingdom of Israel (1 Kings 16:29)
36. "For my flesh is _____ food" (John 6:55 NIV)
38. "In vain the _____ is spread" (Prov. 1:17)
42. Amorite king of Bashan (Deut. 31:4)

by Janet Kennedy

ACROSS

1. What the Israelites did in Egypt
8. Preposition
9. "For the kingdom of heaven is ____ hand" (Matt. 3:2)
10. Rural Electrification Administration, abbr.
12. Simile preposition
13. "And thou shalt make a hanging . . .wrought with ____ " (Exod. 26:36)
17. "And his raiment became. . . exceeding white . . .so as no ____ . . . can white them (Mark 9:3)
18. Inspector General, abbr.
20. "Saying [to Philip], ____, we would see Jesus" (John 12:21)
22. Each, abbr.
23. These people built a house for David (2 Sam. 5:11)
28. Railroad, abbr.
29. "They. . .bought with [the money] the ____ field, to bury strangers in" (Matt. 27:7)
30. South Dakota, abbr.
31. Institute, abbr.
34. "Esau, who is ____ " (Gen. 36:1)
36. People with the same profession as Simon (Acts 9:43)
39. "He that heareth the word, and ____ with joy receiveth it" (Matt. 13:20)
40. "Though they be ____ like crimson" (Isa. 1:18)
41. Alcoholics Anonymous, abbr.
42. Common Era, abbr.
43. Stitching a picture on cloth
48. "It is a ____ thing that the king requireth" (Dan. 2:11)
50. "He stood by the ____ of Gennesaret" (Luke 5:1)
51. Streets, abbr.
52. Persons who fill seams or joints so they will not leak

DOWN

1. People who work with brass
2. Impersonal pronoun
3. People who make candies, cake, etc. for sale
4. A vegetable which looks similar to spinach
5. Repetitive
6. An earner
7. "And Pharaoh was wroth against . . .the chief of the butlers, and against the chief of the ____ " (Gen. 40:2)
11. More, suffix
14. Good; well; true, prefix
15. Elevated railroad
16. 550, Rom. num.
19. People who grow flowers and vegetables
21. Internal Revenue Service, abbr.
24. Revolutions per second, abbr.
25. "We are the clay, and thou our ____; and we all are the work of thy hand" (Isa. 64:8)
26. And, Lat.
27. A person between 13 and 19
32. Measurement at sea, abbr.
33. "____ ____ can you see?" (2 words)
35. "Why ____ the heathen rage?" (Ps. 2:1)
37. "Why make ye this ____, and weep?" (Mark 5:39)
38. More scarce
39. Alternating current, abbr.
40. Rubidium, chem. symbol
44. "Jesus. . .findeth Philip, and saith unto him, Follow ____ " (John 1:43)

45. Not well
46. A relay type of transportation of men or horses in India
47. _____ out: barely making a living
49. Preposition showing location or time

PUZZLE 26

by Teri Grottke

ACROSS

1. Jacob's other name
5. Mr., Sp. abbr.
7. Selenium, chem. symbol
9. Middle Latin, abbr.
10. "The gift. . .perverteth the words of the ____" (Exod. 23:8)
13. "Tola the son of ____" (Judg. 10:1)
16. Concise
17. Each, abbr.
18. "For the statues of ____" (Mic. 6:16)
19. Neon, chem. symbol
20. Wisconsin, abbr.
21. Antimony, chem. symbol
22. "Why dost thou. . .cause me to behold ____?" (Hab. 1:3)
26. "Great well that is in ____" (1 Sam. 19:22)
28. "Melech, and ____, and Ahaz" (1 Chron. 8:35)
30. "Rekem, and ____, and Taralah" (Josh. 18:27)
32. Boy
34. "We were willing to have imparted unto you. . .also ____ own souls" (1 Thess. 2:8)
36. Conjunction
37. "One that is proud and ____" (Isa. 2:12)
41. "Will he ____ thy riches?" (Job 36:19)
44. Adam's wife
45. Where Joseph, Mary, and Jesus went to escape Herod
47. Not him
48. "Barley was in the ____" (Exod. 9:31)
51. Smallest state, abbr.
52. Impossible to deny
57. "____ thy cause with thy neighbour" (Prov. 25:9)
58. "Your own husbands. . .may without the word be ____ by the conversation of the wives" (1 Pet. 3:1)

DOWN

1. "But without faith it is ____" (Heb. 11:6)
2. "God hath given them the spirit of ____" (Rom. 11:8)
3. Judah's firstborn (Gen. 38:6)
4. "____, and Shimei" (Num. 3:18)
5. "Then the ____ said within himself, What shall I do?" (Luke 16:3)
6. "I. . .will ____ them as silver" (Zech. 13:9)
7. "If any man will ____ thee at the law" (Matt. 5:40)
8. "Out of the mount of ____?" (Obad. 8)
11. "____ them that love us" (Titus 3:15)
12. A greeting
14. Argon, chem. symbol
15. "Hosanna in the ____" (Mark 11:10)
23. "Ye tithe mint and ____" (Luke 11:42)
24. Organization to assist those who have served in the armed forces, abbr.
25. "Pass ye unto ____, and see" (Amos 6:2)
27. Condition that affects motor coordination, abbr.
29. Part of the Freudian psyche
31. "For, ____, the winter is past" (Song of Sol. 2:11)

33. "Doe, ____ ____, a female deer, Re . . ." (2 words)
35. Say again
36. Preposition
38. Above
39. "I ____ the Lord" (Jon. 1:9)
40. You, King James Eng.
42. Address abbreviation
43. Magnetic resonance imaging, abbr.
46. Food, slang
49. Moses parted the ____ Sea
50. Peninsula state, abbr.
52. "____ thou count me therefore" (Philem. 17)

53. Iron, chem. symbol
54. Tantalum, chem. symbol
55. "Lest. . .I myself should ____ a castaway . . ." (1 Cor. 9:27)
56. Enlisted woman, abbr.

PUZZLE 27

by Mary Louise DeMott

ACROSS

1. "Seeking goodly ____" (Matt. 13:45)
2. This Bible treasure is the last stone inserted in the High Priest's breastplate (Exod. 28:17–20)
12. Be
14. People or things close at hand
15. Department of Defense, abbr.
16. Seventeenth letter of the Greek alphabet
18. American Kennel Club, abbr.
19. Commercials, in other words, for short
20. These Bible treasures are plants with leaves or seeds used for food
22. A statement the speaker knows to be untrue
23. Thirteenth letter of the Greek alphabet
24. Rather gray
26. Doctor's degree
27. Emperor of Russia
29. Woodwind instrument of treble pitch
31. Woman church leader
32. A coagulated mass
34. Every one
37. Abbreviation of 34 Across
38. This Bible treasure is a rich green color, the first stone in the second row of the High Priest's breastplate (Exod. 28:17–20)
43. Old English, abbr.
44. Ribonucleic acid, abbr.
46. Iridescent gems
47. Opposite of nay
48. Yards, abbr.
49. "And ____ did that which was right" (1 Kings 15:11)
50. Creator and ruler of the universe
51. A rope with a running noose
54. This Bible treasure is beautifully veined, semi-transparent, a variety of quartz (Exod. 28:17–20)
56. A guarantee
57. Trapped

DOWN

1. Boring teacher
2. Second book of the OT
3. Helps
4. Recording Secretary, abbr.
5. Lieutenant, abbr.
7. Preposition
8. Hush
9. Loud ringing of a bell
10. A member of a people living near the arctic coast of North America and eastern Siberia
11. Shrink back
13. Apple-green chalcedony
16. Rural Electrification Administration, abbr.
17. A bright broad sash worn with a kimono
20. House of Representatives, abbr.
21. Religious education, in other words, abbr.
24. A diving bird
25. Watered or sprayed
28. Fuss, trouble, excitement
30. Boy Scouts of America, abbr.
32. These Bible treasures, found in the High Priest's breastplate, are identical to the emerald except in color, a light or bluish green (Exod. 28:17–20)

33. A four wheeled carriage with a folding top
35. North American prairie wolf
36. Paid careful attention to
39. Central state whose capital is Jefferson City, abbr.
40. Environmental Protection Agency, abbr.
41. Montgomery's state, abbr.
42. Left side, abbr.
45. Autonomous Soviet Socialist Republic, abbr.
47. A gelatinous substance, from sea-weed, used as a laxative

52. Selenium, chem. symbol
53. Writings that belong to both Jews and Christians, abbr.
54. Article used before a vowel
55. Peach state, abbr.

PUZZLE 28

by Janet W. Adkins

ACROSS

1. "The children of the _____ were gathered together" (Judg. 6:33)
5. "Why _____ ye not the breaches of the house?" (2 Kings 12:7)
7. "I cannot redeem it for myself, lest I _____ mine own inheritance" (Ruth 4:6)
8. A son of Helem (1 Chron. 7:35)
10. "How _____ I endure to see the destruction of my kindred?" (Esther 8:6)
11. Moves covertly
13. Etruscan god
14. "And they straightway left their _____, and followed him" (Matt. 4:20)
15. A Babylonian chief god
17. "_____, with Sapphira his wife, sold a possession" (Acts 5:1)
19. "And Josiah gave to the people, of the flock, _____ and kids" (2 Chron. 35:7)
21. Doctor's degree
22. "Go to the _____, thou sluggard" (Prov. 6:6)
23. Capuchin monkey
24. Artificial language
25. "Even upon his forefront, did he put the golden _____" (Lev. 8:9)
27. Political representative
29. "Of _____, the family of the Erites" (Num. 26:16)
30. "Have they not _____?" (Judg. 5:30)
31. "Of every tree of the garden thou mayest freely _____" (Gen. 2:16)
32. A vessel in which substances are pounded
34. "He shall not search whether it be good or _____" (Lev. 27:33)
35. "And the priest may bring her _____ and set her before the Lord" (Num. 5:16)
36. Swiss river
37. "Bear your iniquities, even forty years, and ye shall know my _____ of promise" (Num. 14:34)
39. Revise, prepare for publication

DOWN

1. Poetic "ever"
2. News agency, abbr.
3. "Gather my _____ together unto me" (Ps. 50:5)
4. "What have I done. . .that thou hast smitten me these three _____?" (Num. 22:28)
5. "And he _____ before, and climbed up into a sycamore tree to see him" (Luke 19:4)
6. Genetic material
7. "Call me not Naomi, call me _____" (Ruth 1:20)
9. Modern Achai in Greece
10. "Her _____ goeth not out by night" (Prov. 31:18)
11. "Nor sitteth in the _____ of the scornful" (Ps. 1:1)
12. "Arphaxad, which was the son of _____, which was the son of Noe" (Luke 3:36)
13. "Thy word is a _____ unto my feet" (Ps. 119:105)
14. "Were there not ten cleansed? but where are the _____?" (Luke 17:17)
16. "Till ye have scattered them _____" (Ezek. 34:21)

18. "And ___ was destroyed of nation, and city of city" (2 Chron. 15:6)
19. "Behold, the people of the ___ now are many" (Exod. 5:5)
20. "Certain lewd fellows of the baser ___" (Acts 17:5)
23. "And Samuel answered Saul, and said, I am the ___" (1 Sam. 9:19)
26. "With a strong hand, and with a stretched out ___" (Ps. 136:12)
27. "He ___ not their soul from death" (Ps. 78:50)

28. "The wild beast shall ___ them" (Hos. 13:8)
30. "They look and ___ upon me" (Ps. 22:17)
33. Confederate soldier Johnny ___
34. ___, humbug!
36. Play division
38. "And Joshua sent men from Jericho to ___" (Josh. 7:2)

PUZZLE 29

by Joyce Handzo

ACROSS

1. "Many shall ____ to and fro" (Dan. 12:4)
3. "An half ____ of land" (1 Sam. 14:14)
6. "And ____ his son reigned" (2 Kings 21:18)
10. "As ____ is written" (Mark 1:2)
11. Certified Public Accountant, abbr.
12. A type of bird that wasn't to be eaten (Lev. 11:13)
14. Master of Arts, abbr.
15. Louisiana, abbr.
17. "The ____ of heaven" (Jer. 33:22)
18. "The children of Gad called the altar ____" (Josh. 22:34)
20. "A Prophet was beforetime called a ____" (1 Sam. 9:9)
21. "____ that believeth on him is not condemned" (John 3:18)
23. "And Jacob ____ his clothes" (Gen. 37:34)
24. "For the grace of God that ____ salvation" (Titus 2:11 NKJV)
27. The sixth note of the musical scale
29. One of the sons of Gad (Gen. 46:16)
30. "A ____ work of a sapphire stone" (Exod. 24:10)
32. "He passed through the midst of ____" (Luke 17:11)
35. "Ye ____ of this world" (John 8:23)
36. "I will nourish you, and your little ____" (Gen. 50:21)
37. North Dakota, abbr.
38. "That which groweth of ____ own accord" (Lev. 25:5)
39. "The mountains skipped like ____" (Ps. 114:4)
41. Northeast, abbr.
42. "Whatsoever a man soweth, that shall he also ____" (Gal. 6:7)
44. "I ____ daily with you" (Matt. 26:55)
46. "I am he that liveth, and was ____" (Rev. 1:18)
48. New Testament language, abbr.
50. "____ ye now believe?" (John 16:31)
52. "The ____ shall take him by the heel" (Job 18:9)
54. "Jael the wife of ____" (Judg. 5:24)
56. "Be ____ with such things as ye have" (Heb. 13:5)
57. "____ the kine to the cart" (1 Sam. 6:7)

DOWN

1. "A pure ____ of water of life" (Rev. 22:1)
2. Utah, abbr.
3. Associated Press, abbr.
4. "____ stilled the people before Moses" (Num. 13:30)
5. Ex Officio, abbr.
6. Army Post Office, abbr.
7. A title before the surname of a married woman
8. "God had sworn with an ____" (Acts 2:30)
9. New York, abbr.
11. "David dwelt in the ____" (1 Chron. 11:7)
13. "Elisha passed to ____" (2 Kings 4:8)
16. Arranged, abbr.
19. "Abram ____ as the Lord had spoken" (Gen. 12:4)

22. "_____ and Medad do prophesy in the camp" (Num. 11:27)
25. "All flesh is as _____" (1 Pet. 1:24)
26. "And I said unto him, _____, thou knowest" (Rev. 7:14)
28. "Why make ye this _____, and weep?" (Mark 5:39)
30. "Neither shall there be any more _____" (Rev. 21:4)
31. Vessel, abbr.
32. "The _____ beguiled me" (Gen. 3:13)
33. "_____ did that which was right in the eyes of the LORD" (1 Kings 15:11)

34. "He will _____ them with his troops" (Hab. 3:16)
40. "I am come that they _____ have life" (John 10:10)
42. Rear Admiral, abbr.
43. "Escaped the _____ of the sword" (Heb. 11:34)
45. "The unclean spirit had _____ him" (Mark 1:26)
47. A period of time
49. One of the men who was not with Adonijah (1 Kings 1:8)
51. Alternating Current, abbr.
53. "_____ the beginning" (Gen. 1:1)
55. "Let there _____ light" (Gen. 1:3)

by Janet Kennedy

ACROSS

1. "Though they be red like ____, they shall be as wool" (Isa. 1:18)
6. "Thou shalt also make a laver of ____" (Exod. 30:18)
10. Omissions excepted, abbr.
11. A long period of time
12. "And thou shalt make a veil of ____, and purple" (Exod. 26:31)
13. Lead, chem. symbol
14. Upper case, abbr.
15. Association of American Railroads, abbr.
16. Californian city, abbr.
17. "Lydia, a seller of ____" (Acts 16:14)
19. Academy, abbr.
20. ____ out: barely making a living
22. Kiloliter, abbr.
23. Elevated railroad
24. "And in the place of the boil there be a. . .spot. . .somewhat ____" (Lev. 13:19)
28. Consumed
29. Actress McGraw
30. "They had on their heads crowns of ____" (Rev. 4:4)
32. Base hit (baseball), abbr.
33. "A dove. . .her feathers with ____ gold" (Ps. 68:13)
34. 6, Rom. num.
35. "He. . .saw a publican, named ____. . .and said unto him, Follow me" (Luke 5:27)
38. A liquid adhesive
40. "Of the tribe of ____ were sealed twelve thousand" (Rev. 7:6)
42. "The same came therefore to Philip, . . .saying, ____, we would see Jesus" (John 12:21)
44. "Lie down in ____ pastures" (Ps. 23:2)
47. Bear, Sp.
48. Estimated time of arrival, abbr.
49. "Neither knoweth ____ man the Father, save the Son" (Matt. 11:27)
50. Uncooked
51. "But let your yea be yea; and your ____ . . ." (James 5:12)
52. But
53. "Let not the ____ go down upon your wrath" (Eph. 4:26)

DOWN

1. "Two vessels of fine ____, precious as gold" (Ezra 8:27)
2. "He ____ the sea, and maketh it dry" (Nah. 1:4)
3. "Come unto ____, all ye that labour" (Matt. 11:28)
4. "Be in health, even as thy ____ prospereth" (3 John 2)
5. "For Christ also hath ____ suffered for sins" (1 Pet. 3:18)
6. "Canst not make one hair white or ____" (Matt. 5:36)
7. Country area
8. At the age of, abbr.
9. "They clothed Daniel with ____, and put a chain of gold about his neck" (Dan. 5:29)
12. Sound of sheep
18. "Though they be ____ like crimson, they shall be as wool" (Isa. 1:18)
21. An interjection of surprise
23. And, Lat.
25. "One ____ is with the Lord as a thousand years" (2 Pet. 3:8)
26. Able, suffix

27. "Peter said, _____ and gold have I none; but such as I have give I thee" (Acts 3:6)
28. Those who give counsel
30. "I saw seven _____ candlesticks" (Rev. 1:12)
31. "_____ no man any thing, but to love one another" (Rom. 13:8)
32. "He made for the altar a _____ grate" (Exod. 38:4)
36. Southern state, abbr.
37. "I will pass through. . .removing . . .all the _____ cattle among the sheep" (Gen. 30:32)

38. "Yea, _____ hairs are here and there upon him, yet he knoweth not" (Hos. 7:9)
39. Repulsive to the eye
41. Jacob's brother
43. Independent T.V. Authority, abbr.
45. Take food
46. Empire state, abbr.

PUZZLE **31**

By Joyce Handzo

ACROSS

1. "Take up thy ____, and walk" (John 5:8)
3. "They were ____ asunder" (Heb. 11:37)
6. "Casting all your ____ upon him" (1 Pet. 5:7)
9. "A continual dropping in a very ____ day and a contentious woman are alike" (Prov. 27:15)
11. Preposition
12. Underwriters Laboratories, abbr.
13. "Joshua sent men from Jericho to ____" (Josh. 7:2)
15. A wager
16. "God made them male and ____" (Mark 10:6)
18. South Dakota, abbr.
19. "My foot standeth in an ____ place" (Ps. 26:12)
21. The desert area in southern Israel
22. "Thou shalt make a ____ of pure gold" (Exod. 28:36)
24. Associated Press, abbr.
26. Ripped
27. "Touch the ____ of his garment" (Matt. 14:36)
28. "The ____ of the land is gone" (Isa. 24:11)
30. Tin, chem. symbol
31. "They found a plain in the land of ____" (Gen. 11:2)
34. "The Lord said unto Moses in ____" (Exod. 4:19)
36. A different spelling of Jehovah
38. Old covenant writings, abbr.
39. To ooze gently
41. A stringed musical instrument
43. "Will they not say that ye are ____?" (1 Cor. 14:23)

45. A religious service held in late afternoon
47. "One ____ contained forty baths" (1 Kings 7:38)
49. "Go thee one way ____ other" (Ezek. 21:16)
50. Electrical engineer, abbr.
51. The top of a hill or wave
52. "Prepare ye the ____ of the Lord" (Matt. 3:3)
53. "With God ____ things are possible" (Mark 10:27)
54. "Till a ____ strike through his liver" (Prov. 7:23)

DOWN

1. "Do not they ____ that worthy name?" (James 2:7)
2. Physician's title, abbr.
3. "Corn is sifted in a ____" (Amos 9:9)
4. Prefix meaning before
5. Cheyenne's state, abbr.
6. "Joy ____ in the morning" (Ps. 30:5)
7. "We wrestle not against flesh and blood, but. . .the ____ of the darkness" (Eph. 6:12)
8. "And about the ____ hour he went out" (Matt. 20:6)
10. To help, especially in bad conduct
11. "Ye shall have tribulation ____ days" (Rev. 2:10)
14. "An ____ soul shall suffer hunger" (Prov. 19:15)
17. "They would have repented long ____" (Matt. 11:21)
20. "He went into a city called ____" (Luke 7:11)
23. "I ____ Alpha and Omega" (Rev. 22:13)

by Janet Adkins

ACROSS

1. "And Adam called his wife's name
   ____" (Gen. 3:20)
4. "____, the family of the Punites"
   (Num. 26:23)
7. "And ____. . .did evil. . .above all
   that were before him"
   (1 Kings 16:30)
11. "What seemeth you ____ I will do"
    (2 Sam. 18:4)
13. "There was no room for them in the
    ___" (Luke 2:7)
14. "The price of his ____ shall be
    according unto the number of years"
    (Lev. 25:50)
15. ____ Stanley Gardner
16. Alfonzo's queen
17. Irish Gaelic
18. "He wrote also letters to ____ on the
    Lord God of Israel"
    (2 Chron. 32:17)
19. "I have perfumed my bed with myrrh,
    aloes, and ____" (Prov. 7:17)
21. Sarah might have called her husband
    ____ for short
23. That is, Lat. abbr.
24. "____ off all his hair" (Lev. 14:8)
27. "Martha, thou art ____. . .about many
    things" (Luke 10:41)
32. "Bring the tribe of ____ near, and
    present them before Aaron the priest"
    (Num. 3:6)
33. "But it ____ thou, a man mine equal"
    (Ps. 55:13)
34. "____ that man, and have no
    company with him" (2 Thess. 3:14)
35. "Wrought with labour and ____ night
    and day" (2 Thess. 3:8)
37. "Cursed is every one that hangeth on
    ____ ____ " (Gal. 3:13) (2 words)
38. Doctor's assistant, abbr.
39. "A bird of the ____ shall carry the
    voice" (Eccles. 10:20)
40. "The ____ shall melt with fervent
    heat" (2 Pet. 3:12)

45. "Abner went also to speak in the
    ____ of David" (2 Sam. 3:19)
49. "There come in also a poor man in
    ____ raiment" (James 2:2)
50. Belonging to the first son of Judah
    (Gen. 38:3)
51. "When he speaketh ____ ____
    he speaketh of his own" (John 8:44)
    (2 words)
52. "The same is Micaiah the son of
    ____" (2 Chron. 18:7)
53. "Bind them. . .upon thine heart, and
    ____ them about thy neck"
    (Prov. 6:21)
54. Ocean movement
55. "Neither rend your clothes; ____ ye
    die" (Lev. 10:6)
56. Her Majesty's ship, abbr.
57. Air, prefix

DOWN

1. "And ships shall come. . .and shall
   afflict ____" (Num. 24:24)
2. Woman's name
3. Father of Naum (Luke 3:25)
4. "For a ____ of bread that man will
   transgress" (Prov. 28:21)
5. "Also Bakbukiah and ____, their
   brethren, were over against them"
   (Neh. 12:9)
6. "____, with Sapphira his wife, sold a
   possession" (Acts 5:1)
7. "There was ____ ____ of glass like
   unto crystal" (Rev. 4:6) (2 words)
8. "Do thyself no ____: for we are all
   here" (Acts 16:28)
9. "There come in ____ a poor man"
   (James 2:2)
10. "They took knowledge of them, that
    they had ____ with Jesus"
    (Acts 4:13)
12. Seaport in W. Israel, formerly Jaffa
20. "Abner the son of ____"
    (1 Kings 2:32)
22. "____ merciful, O Lord, unto thy
    people Israel" (Deut. 21:8)
24. Weatherman's abbreviation

25. "Rachel weeping for _____ children" (Matt. 2:18)
26. "And the king of Assyria brought men from Babylon, . . .Cuthah, . . . and from _____" (2 Kings 17:24)
27. "Silent" _____ Coolidge
28. To petition, supplicate
29. "_____ I am meek and lowly in heart" (Matt. 11:29)
30. Shoshonean
31. Confederate general
33. "He that _____ souls is wise" (Prov. 11:30)
36. "The mighty _____ gathered against me" (Ps. 59:3)
37. "The men went up and viewed _____" (Josh. 7:2)

39. "And the _____ of Kish. . .were lost" (1 Sam. 9:3)
40. "So thou shalt put away _____ from among you" (Deut. 22:24)
41. "He burned the bones of the king of Edom into _____" (Amos 2:1)
42. House additions
43. "And make me savoury _____, such as I love" (Gen. 27:4)
44. Cut
46. Other, Lat.
47. "And he made him to _____ in the second chariot" (Gen. 41:43)
48. "For he that is now called a Prophet was beforetime called a _____" (1 Sam. 9:9)

PUZZLE 33

by Teri Grottke

ACROSS

1. Belonging to the father of Leah & Rachel (Gen. 29)
7. Kansas City, abbr.
9. Son of Abda (1 Kings 4:6)
11. Eosinophil, abbr.
13. South, abbr.
14. Indium, chem. symbol
15. Son of Noah
17. Royal Military College, abbr.
18. Comes after spring
21. "The wall of ____" (Amos 1:14)
23. Beryllium, chem. symbol
24. City near Bethel
25. Bind
26. "Destroy ____ kings and people" (Ezra 6:12)
27. Preposition
29. Belonging to Jacob's first wife (Gen. 29)
33. "____ that ye refuse not him that speaketh" (Heb. 12:25)
34. Village in Simeon (1 Chron. 4:32)
36. Very warm
37. Belonging to Eve's husband
39. "____ are spies" (Gen. 42:9)
40. Iridium, chem. symbol
41. Before, poetic
43. An altar (Josh. 22)
45. Arsenic, chem. symbol
46. "It shall no more be called. . .the valley of the son of____" (Jer. 7:32)
49. "For ____ is ordained. . ." (Isa. 30:33)
52. Recede
53. A thousand thousands, abbr.
55. Ordinance Officer, abbr.
56. Mister, abbr.
57. Length overall, abbr.
58. Mother-of-pearl
60. Exposure index, abbr.
61. Picosecond, abbr.
62. Convulsion
63. Nanogram, abbr.

DOWN

1. "For, ____, the winter is past" (Song of Sol. 2:11)
2. "Eshtemoh, and ____" (Josh. 15:50)
3. Moza's son (1 Chron. 8:37)
4. Capital of Moab (Num. 21:28)
5. No, slang
6. Intelligent
7. Edge of the road, Br. spelling
8. Deep unconsciousness
9. Donkey
10. Duplicated
12. School, abbr.
16. Letters, etc.
19. Menan's son (Luke 3:31)
20. Brawl
22. Buzzing stinger
26. Solomon's great-grandson (Matt. 1:7)
28. No, old English
30. Ahitub's son (1 Sam. 14:3)
31. Equestrians
32. Address abbreviation
34. "____ begat Aram" (Matt. 1:3)
35. Encounter
38. "And, lo, three ____ stood by him" (Gen. 18:2)
42. A race of giants
44. Entrances
46. "Another to ____ him up" (Eccles. 4:10)
47. Members of a Nigerian tribe
48. Basketball organization, abbr.
50. A composition in verse

51. Advanced mathematics, abbr.
54. Where a child likes to sit
59. San Diego's state, abbr.

PUZZLE 34

by Janet Kennedy

ACROSS

1. "Ye who ____ were far off are made nigh" (Eph. 2:13)
9. Car manufacturing union, abbr.
12. Removal of a mistake
13. Book that follows Daniel
15. Electrical engineer, abbr.
16. Memphis' state, abbr.
17. Not here
19. "____, and ye shall find," (Matt. 7:7)
21. Contraction for I have
23. "I ____ the Lord, and he heard me" (Ps. 34:4)
27. West Indies, abbr.
28. "The eye cannot say unto the hand, I have no ____ of thee" (1 Cor. 12:21)
29. Article
30. A long, low soft couch or sofa
31. Geomagnetic electrokinetograph, abbr.
32. Book, abbr.
34. Inspector General, abbr.
35. Letter of the alphabet before "en"
37. "Jesus saith unto her, . . .whom ____ thou?" (John 20:15)
39. "Like the ____ birth of a woman" (Ps. 58:8)
40. Foot, suffix
41. Mercury, chem. symbol
42. "And Joshua sent men from Jericho to ____" (Josh. 7:2)
43. "But ____ for the promise of the Father" (Acts 1:4)
44. "My heart is like wax; ____ is melted" (Ps. 22:14)
46. "Make me as one of thy ____ servants" (Luke 15:19)
47. Royal Horse Guard, abbr.
49. "[Abram] sat in the ____ door in the heat of the day" (Gen. 18:1)
51. Center fielder (baseball), abbr.
52. "Therefore ____ said unto Samuel, Go, lie down. . .if he call thee. . .say, speak, Lord" (1 Sam. 3:9)
54. "For my yoke is ____, and my burden is light" (Matt. 11:30)
55. "And the people ____ for Zacharias, . . .he tarried so long" (Luke 1:21)

DOWN

1. "As a roaring lion. . .____ whom he may devour" (1 Pet. 5:8)
2. A rock or soil containing some metal
3. Mother
4. This, Sp.
5. Musical ditties
6. Iridium, chem. symbol
7. Encountered
8. "The woman was a Greek, . . .and ____ besought [Jesus] that he would cast forth the devil" (Mark 7:26)
9. Took advantage of
10. First 2 vowels
11. "So that ye come behind in no gift; ____ for the coming of our Lord" (1 Cor. 1:7)
14. Either
18. To squeeze with the arms
19. "There is none that ____ after God" (Rom. 3:11)
20. A valuable tree of Hawaii
22. Symbol of victory
24. "Lord I believe; help thou mine ____" (Mark 9:24)

25. Hand, abbr.
26. "No man hath seen God at any ____" (John 1:18)
27. "Our soul ____ for the Lord; he is our help" (Ps. 33:20)
33. "He opened not the doors. . . therefore they took a ____, and opened them" (Judg. 3:25)
36. "A sound from heaven as of a rushing ____ wind" (Acts 2:2)
37. "Find me, when ye shall ____ for me with all your heart" (Jer. 29:13)
38. "I will pour out of my ____ upon all flesh" (Acts 2:17)

39. Bring together into one
45. A hot or cold beverage
48. "In the beginning ____ created the heavens and the earth" (Gen. 1:1)
50. Maritime province, abbr.
52. Apiece, in other words, abbr.
53. 51, Rom. num.

PUZZLE 35

by Janet W. Adkins

ACROSS

1. "For there is nothing. . .____, that shall not be known" (Matt. 10:26)
4. "Wizards that ____, and that mutter" (Isa. 8:19)
8. Same, prefix
12. "Why make ye this ____, and weep?" (Mark 5:39)
13. Belonging to Adam's wife
14. Book that follows Joel
15. Third son of Levi (Gen. 46:11)
17. Plan
19. Handle of a weapon
21. "For, lo, I will ____ up a shepherd in the land" (Zech. 11:16)
22. An aromatic herb
25. "Learn to maintain good works for necessary ____" (Titus 3:14)
27. "For this ____ is Mount Sinai in Arabia" (Gal. 4:25)
28. Pocket bread
29. "The ____ of violence is in their hands" (Isa. 59:6)
32. "____ that thou forget not the Lord thy God" (Deut. 8:11)
34. Father of Mahath (1 Chron. 6:35)
36. "____, Lord: yet the dogs. . .eat of the children's crumbs" (Mark 7:28)
37. "Then Pharaoh's ____ was come forth out of Egypt" (Jer. 37:5)
39. "Let us not ____ it, but cast lots for it" (John 19:24)
40. "Which in other ____ was not made known unto the sons of men" (Eph. 3:5)
41. "Not with broided hair, or gold, or pearls, or costly ____" (1 Tim. 2:9)
42. "As I wrote ____ in few words" (Eph. 3:3)

45. Angel's aura
47. "____ the spoil of your enemies with your brethren" (Josh. 22:8)
49. "Their ____ are desolate" (Zeph. 3:6)
53. Thoroughfares, abbr.
54. Existed
56. Furnish with special gear
57. Only
58. Naked
59. "My ____ also will I spread upon him" (Ezek. 12:13)

DOWN

1. "And Noah begat Shem, ____, and Japheth" (Gen. 5:32)
2. Chemical suffix
3. "The inhabitants of ____ and her towns" (Josh. 17:11)
4. "Who shall separate us from the love of Christ? shall. . .famine, or nakedness, or ____, or sword?" (Rom. 8:35)
5. "Deliver me, O Lord, from the ____ man" (Ps. 140:1)
6. Electrical engineer, abbr.
7. Letter addendums, abbr.
8. Words that can be laughter or scorn (Job 39:25)
9. Buddhist sacred mountain
10. Mothers
11. "In ____, I will call them my people, which were not my people" (Rom. 9:25)
16. "____ the son of Enan" (Num. 1:15)
18. The yellowish fatty part of milk
20. Parson bird
22. Infant
23. "After him was Shammah the son of ____" (2 Sam. 23:11)
24. "Sawed with ____" (1 Kings 7:9)

26. "____, and I will tell thee what the Lord hath said to me this night" (1 Sam. 15:16)
28. Father, Fr.
29. Tribe of Anna the prophetess (Luke 2:36)
30. "There was a marriage in ____ of Galilee" (John 2:1)
31. Neat
33. "The heathen ____" (Ps. 46:6)
35. "Nor shoot an ____ there" (2 Kings 19:32)
38. Melanocyte-stimulating hormone, abbr.
40. "____, O God, judge the earth" (Ps. 82:68)

41. "Who can forgive sins, but God ____?" (Luke 5:21)
42. "For ____ was first formed, then Eve" (1 Tim. 2:13)
43. "Wilt thou destroy all the city for lack of ____?" (Gen. 18:28)
44. "The Lord will pass ____ the door" (Exod. 12:23)
46. "The children of ____, the children of Talmon" (Ezek. 2:42)
48. Recede
50. Sea eagle
51. "But the wheat and the ____ were not smitten" (Exod. 9:32)
52. A noncommissioned officer, abbr.
55. Apiece, in other words, abbr.

PUZZLE 36

by Janet Kennedy

ACROSS

1. "As the ____ ____ for silver, and the furnace for gold" (Prov. 27:21)
7. Proof of who you are, abbr.
9. Woman's name
10. "Open up and say ____"
12. Nickel, chem. symbol
13. With reference to, abbr.
14. "The pots also, and the shovels, and the ____" (2 Chron. 4:16)
17. Consume
18. Mountain, abbr.
19. Way to cook meat
20. "A man that beareth false witness. . .is a ____, and a sword" (Prov. 25:18)
22. Task force, abbr.
23. "And pierce his ear with an ____" (Exod. 21:6 NIV)
25. "They sacrifice. . .under oaks, and poplars and ____" (Hos. 4:13)
28. Compass point, abbr.
31. Father
32. "From ____ the face of the earth" (Gen. 7:4)
34. "She layeth her hands to the ____, and her hands hold the distaff" (Prov. 31:19)
37. Tellurium, chem. symbol
39. "It were better for him that a ____ were hanged about his neck" (Luke 17:2)
41. A short time of sleep
42. Preposition
43. Californian city, abbr.
44. "For the ____ which is lent to the Lord" (1 Sam. 2:20)
46. Building cooler, abbr.
48. "Hide them in the clay in the ____" (Jer. 43:9)
52. "Gideon threshed wheat by the ____" (Judg. 6:11)
53. New, prefix

DOWN

1. "The basins, and the ____, and the bowls, and the caldrons" (Jer. 52:19)
2. A thought
3. Northern continent, abbr.
4. Nothing
5. "Shouldest bray a fool in a mortar among wheat with a ____" (Prov. 27:22)
6. Asian goat
7. Draws with a black liquid
8. "Her hands to the spindle, and her hands hold the ____" (Prov. 31:19)
11. Makes an owl's cry
15. A large Australian bird resembling an ostrich
16. Simpleton
21. "Fear not, . . .arise, go up to ____" (Josh. 8:1)
24. "Jesus ____" (John 11:35)
26. Long playing phonograph record, abbr.
27. "Yet they had a file for the ____, and for the coulters" (1 Sam. 13:21)
29. To remove men from a ship
30. Building wing
33. "Come near, . . .that I may ____ thee, my son, whether thou be . . .Esau" (Gen. 27:21)
35. "Let him ____ his foot in oil" (Deut. 33:24)

36. "Samuel. . .arose and went to _____, and said, Here am I" (1 Sam. 3:8)
38. A very long period of time
40. "The sluggard will not _____ by reason of the cold" (Prov. 20:4)
41. "He went into a city called _____" (Luke 7:11)
45. Make a mistake
46. American Cancer Society, abbr.
47. Noise
48. The temperature at which a liquid boils, abbr.
49. That is, Lat. abbr.
50. Article, Fr.

51. "_____ man can serve two masters" (Matt. 6:24)

by Mary Louise DeMott

ACROSS

1. This spiritual fruit means to bear provocation patiently
10. Diving bird with loud wild cry
11. White, foot-length robes worn by some Christian priests
12. Loose-fitting brightly colored shirt
13. Family doctor, for instance, abbr.
15. Rooms, abbr.
17. Philadelphia's state, abbr.
18. Do, ____, mi
19. This spiritual fruit means a deep emotion of pleasure
20. That is, Lat. abbr.
22. Young adults, abbr.
25. Either
26. Myself
27. Church, abbr.
29. An exclamation of surprise, delight, or pain
30. To perform or carry out
31. Juno's state, abbr.
32. Verity
33. Nautical mile, abbr.
34. Memphis' state, abbr.
35. Dorothy's state, abbr.
36. Beast of burden
38. Each, abbr.
39. Suffix that means "dear little one"
40. Girl Scouts of America, abbr.
42. Tin, chem. symbol
43. Osmium, chem. symbol
44. Miami's state, abbr.
45. Prosecuting officer, in other words, abbr.
47. Silicon, chem. symbol
48. Anne of Green Gables province, abbr.
49. Excessively submissive

51. A mark left where a wound has healed
52. Makes a living laboriously
54. "The kingdom of God is. . .____, and peace, and joy" (Rom. 14:17)

DOWN

1. A flow of tears
2. National League, abbr.
3. Creator and ruler of universe
4. Used for washing and cleaning things
5. To take back or retract
6. Carnivals
7. A Swedish woman's name
8. Runs batted in, in baseball, abbr.
9. Longest book of prophecy, abbr.
13. This spiritual fruit means the quality of being good
14. People with uncontrollable impulse to set things on fire
16. This spiritual fruit means quietness and obedience
21. Actinium, chem. symbol
23. Has common boundaries
24. An exclamation of doubt, inquiry, or surprise
28. Heights, abbr.
29. An exclamation of surprise or exultation
35. Blue grass state, abbr.
37. Christian, abbr.
40. Angry stare
41. Good-bye, Fr.
44. Flavorless
46. Inquires
49. School, abbr.
50. Egg layer
51. Surgeon general, abbr.
53. Compass point, abbr.

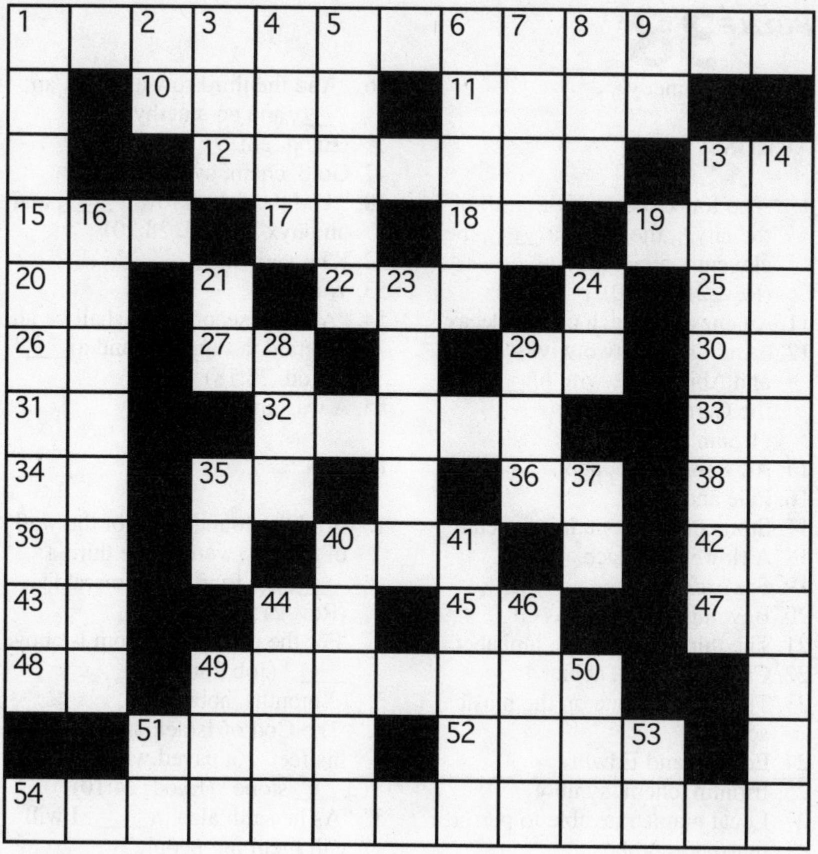

PUZZLE **38**

by Janet Kennedy

ACROSS

1. "The foundations of the wall of the city. . .the tenth, a ____, the eleventh, a jacinth" (Rev. 21:19–20)
11. An enzyme which causes decay
12. "And David's two wives. . . and Abigail the wife of ____ the Carmelite" (1 Sam. 30:5)
14. Air Force Base, abbr.
16. Pale and wan
17. Stone or soil containing metal
18. A flower necklace
19. For each
20. Beverage
21. The third letter of the alphabet
22. City of Angels, abbr.
23. The seventh tone on the musical scale
24. Edward and Edwin
25. Iridium, chem. symbol
27. Local magistrate able to perform marriages, abbr.
29. "____ man hath seen God at any time" (John 1:18)
31. Prefix: twice, double
32. Prefix: again, once more
33. "The first foundation was ____" (Rev. 21:19)
35. Unity, agreement
38. National Guard, abbr.
39. Third day of the week, abbr.
40. "Out of the ____ palaces" (Ps. 45:8)
43. Reverence
44. "But they that wait upon the Lord shall ____ their strength" (Isa. 40:31)

46. "And the third row a ligure, an ____, and an amethyst" (Exod. 28:19)
47. Gold, chem. symbol
48. "And the fourth row a ____, and an onyx" (Exod. 28:20)
52. KJV verb suffix
53. Wager
54. "And the second row shall be an emerald, a sapphire, and a ____" (Exod. 28:18)
55. A washing of the body

DOWN

1. "And the foundations of the wall of the city were. . .the third a ____; the fourth, an emerald" (Rev. 21:19)
2. "For the price of wisdom is above ____" (Job 28:18)
3. 12 months, abbr.
4. "The God of Israel: and. . .under his feet. . .a paved work of a ____ stone" (Exod. 24:10)
5. "As he saith also in ____, I will call them my people" (Rom. 9:25)
6. "And the twelve gates were twelve pearls; every. . .gate was of one ____" (Rev. 21:21)
7. "Wisdom cannot be valued with the ____" (Job 28:16)
8. Southern continent, abbr.
9. A submarine
10. "And he that sat was to look upon like a jasper and a ____ stone" (Rev. 4:3)
13. Man's name
15. "And there was an herd of many swine ____ on the mountain" (Luke 8:32)

26. "Come unto me, . . .and I will give you ____" (Matt. 11:28)
27. "And the foundations of the wall of the city were. . .the eleventh, a ____; the twelfth, an amethyst" (Rev. 21:19–20)
28. Letter addendum, abbr.
30. Either
34. "Doth the plowman ____ all day to sow?" (Isa. 28:24)
36. "No man also seweth a piece of ____ cloth on an old garment" (Mark 2:21)
37. Swelled or heaved with great force
41. The symbol of victory
42. "My manner of life from my ____" (Acts 26:4)
43. Magic word: ____ - cadabra
45. "Take, ____; this is my body" (Matt. 26:26)
47. Of age, Lat. abbr.
48. Bachelor of Divinity, abbr.
49. A, ____, ____, O, U
50. Young Men's Christian Association, abbr.
51. "____, I am with you alway" (Matt. 28:20)
53. Barium, chem. symbol

Puzzle 39

by Janet W. Adkins

ACROSS

1. Cat comment
5. "Thou ____ cast out in the open field" (Ezek. 16:5)
9. Glass container
12. Johanan's grandfather (Neh. 6:18)
13. "____ begat Asa" (Matt. 1:7)
14. Flightless bird
15. "That thou mayest be clothed, and that the shame of thy ____ do not appear" (Rev. 3:18)
17. Rodent
18. A Latvian
19. "And the ____ shall make you free" (John 8:32)
21. "And the ____ of the locusts were like unto horses" (Rev. 9:7)
24. "For he hath founded it upon the ____, and established it upon the floods" (Ps. 24:2)
25. Buddy
26. Zany
28. "Moses' father in law went up out of the city. . .into the wilderness of Judah, . . .in the south of ____" (Judg. 1:16)
30. "To him which ____ his people through the wilderness" (Ps. 136:16)
31. "And they came to ____, where were twelve wells of water" (Exod. 15:27)
33. "And whosoever shalt exalt himself shall be ____" (Matt. 23:12)
35. Compass direction, abbr.
36. "____, and Dumah, and Eshean" (Josh. 15:52)
37. "For an ____, the hope of salvation" (1 Thess. 5:8)
40. "Certain lewd fellows of the ____ sort" (Acts 17:5)
42. Half, prefix
43. Map abbreviation
44. "And he. . .began to publish in ____ how great things Jesus had done for him" (Mark 5:20)
49. National Stock Exchange, abbr.
50. "Of the tribe of Issachar, ____ the son of Joseph" (Num. 13:7)
51. "Salathiel, which was the son of ____" (Luke 3:27)
52. "Neither did Manasseh drive out the inhabitants of Bethshean. . .nor Taanach. . ., nor the inhabitants of ____" (Judg. 1:27)
53. "Now the ____ of Jacob were twelve" (Gen. 35:22)
54. "Then Herod. . .enquired of them diligently what time the ____ appeared" (Matt. 2:7)

DOWN

1. "The Son of ____ must be lifted up" (John 12:34)
2. Equal Rights Amendment, abbr.
3. "Behold, I saw Absalom hanged in an ____" (2 Sam. 18:10)
4. "Judah is a lion's ____" (Gen. 49:9)
5. "Your messenger, and he that ministered to my ____" (Phil. 2:25)
6. Aid
7. Sibling
8. "If so be ye have ____ that the Lord is gracious" (1 Pet. 2:3)
9. "Abiathar carried the ark of God again to ____" (2 Sam. 15:29)
10. "I ____ ____ the point to die" (Gen. 25:32) (2 words)
11. "The name of the one was Orpah, and the name of the other ____" (Ruth 1:4)
16. River in Scotland
20. "The ____ is not to the swift" (Eccles. 9:11)
21. Health bath
22. "Brought them unto Halah, and Habor, and ____" (1 Chron. 5:26)

23. "There came unto him a woman having an _____ box of very precious ointment" (Matt. 26:7)
24. "Her countenance was no more _____" (1 Sam. 1:18)
26. Little name for a big sea
27. "But ye shall _____ away for your iniquities" (Ezek. 24:23)
29. "For we _____ not make ourselves of the number" (2 Cor. 10:12)
30. This country was once famous for its cedars, abbr.
32. "There _____ him two possessed with devils" (Matt. 8:28)
34. One of the seven churches of Asia
37. Cures
38. Electromagnetic pulse, abbr.
39. "Whose faces were like the faces of _____" (1 Chron. 12:8)
40. "For I was ashamed to require of the king a _____ of soldiers" (Ezra 8:22)
41. "Lord, wilt thou slay _____ a righteous nation?" (Gen. 20:4)
42. Read over hastily
45. Self
46. "_____ there be no strife. . .between me and thee" (Gen. 13:8)
47. "And _____ also the Jairite was a chief ruler about David" (2 Sam. 20:26)
48. "_____, thou hast nothing to draw with" (John 4:11)

PUZZLE 40

by Teri Grottke

ACROSS

1. Has ability
4. "Thou that liftest me up from the ____ of death" (Ps. 9:13)
9. Astatine, chem. symbol
11. A son of Bela (1 Chron. 7:7)
12. "Henoch, and ____, and Eldaah" (1 Chron. 1:33)
13. Fuss
14. A little woman
15. Chief among the captains of David's mighty men (2 Sam. 23:8)
16. "Iniquity of ____ house" (1 Sam. 3:14)
17. A Colossian woman Paul greets (Philem. 2)
19. The Israelites craved this fruit in the wilderness (Num. 11:5)
21. "He shall be like the ____ in the desert" (Jer. 17:6)
22. Sprint
23. Gaius was from here (Acts 20:4)
24. "Their coast was from ____" (Josh. 19:33)
27. "Out of whose womb came the ____?" (Job 38:29)
28. Obadiah, abbr.
30. Account of, abbr.
31. The woman on the scarlet beast had this written on her forehead (Rev. 17:4–5)
34. Race of giants (Deut. 2)
37. Not him
38. "He that is washed needeth not save to wash his feet, but is clean every ____" (John 13:10)
39. Capital of Moab (Num. 21:28)
40. He was the officer over Solomon's household (1 Kings 4:6)
43. Grow
47. Exhaust
48. Also
49. "____ will I sit" (Joel 3:12)
51. Poetic contraction that means early night
52. To stitch
53. Employed
54. Boy

DOWN

1. "Michmash, and ____" (Neh. 11:31)
2. "The gift of ____" (1 Cor. 13:2)
3. Titanium, chem. symbol
4. Someone from Gad
5. Hezron's wife (1 Chron. 2:24)
6. Stannum, other name
7. "Wise men out of ____" (Obad. 8)
8. Southern continent, abbr.
9. Returned exiles (Ezra 2:15)
10. Throw
13. By oneself
15. Jezebel's husband (1 Kings 16:30–31)
16. 6th month of the Hebrew year (Neh. 6:15)
18. Machir's son (1 Chron. 7:16)
20. Before, poetic
23. Unclear
24. A laugh
25. Girl's name
26. Hosea, abbr.
28. Either
29. Near
32. Drop of sadness
33. "He that refuseth reproof ____" (Prov. 10:17)

34. A son of Benjamin (Gen. 46:21)
35. Haze
36. Jesaiah's son (Neh. 11:7)
38. Adverb of location
40. "Of the tribe of ____ were
    sealed" (Rev. 7:6)
41. Length x width
42. Rip
43. Possessive pronoun
44. Greek form of Noah
45. Female bovine
46. Son of Abdiel (1 Chron. 5)
50. An altar (Josh. 22:34)

PUZZLE 41

by Janet Kennedy

ACROSS

1. "Meat offering baken in the ____" (Lev. 2:7)
7. Part of a curved line
9. The sound of a cow
10. "As a man wipeth ____, wiping it, and turning it upside down" (2 Kings 21:13)
12. "My heart standeth in ____ of thy word" (Ps. 119:161)
14. Sweaty smell, in other words
16. Gold, chem. symbol
17. Peach state, abbr.
18. A cow's baby
20. Rounded dishes
21. Old Testament, abbr.
22. "The tongue of the wise ____ knowledge aright" (Prov. 15:2)
24. Electrical engineer, abbr.
25. Compass point, abbr.
26. Tap gently
27. U.S. island commonwealth, abbr.
28. A man's name
31. Dish
34. Velocity, in other words, abbr.
35. Plan again
37. "Certain also of your own ____ have said, For we are also his offspring" (Acts 17:28)
39. By way of
40. "Come unto ____, all ye that labour" (Matt. 11:28)
41. Occupational therapy, abbr.
42. "And he struck it into the pan, or ____, or caldron, or pot" (1 Sam. 2:14)
44. A shady place formed by trees or plants
46. A Catholic sister
48. Of the Navy
50. "____ maketh me to lie down in green pastures" (Ps. 23:2)
51. Mouths or openings, Lat.
52. "For my ____ are many, and my heart is faint" (Lam. 1:22)
53. "Yet they had a file for the. . . ____, and the axes" (1 Sam. 13:21)

DOWN

1. "A ____ of wine" (2 Sam. 6:19)
2. Contraction of I am
3. "____ man hath seen God at any time" (John 1:18)
4. A kind of drinking glass
5. Advertisement, abbr.
6. Nickel, chem. symbol
7. An exclamation of satisfaction
8. "Take thou now the spear. . .and the ____ of water" (1 Sam. 26:11)
11. Cause to be seen
13. "The woman then left her ____, and went her way" (John 4:28)
15. "This do ye, as ____ as ye drink it, in remembrance of me" (1 Cor. 11:25)
16. On guard
18. "Ye hold the tradition of men, as the washing of pots and ____" (Mark 7:8)
19. Belonging to Abia's son (Matt. 1:7)
23. A laugh
27. "Meat offering baken in a ____" (Lev. 2:5)
29. Poem
30. "So the eyes of man are ____ satisfied" (Prov. 27:20)

31. "Make clean the outside of the cup and the ____" (Luke 11:39)
32. California city, abbr.
33. "Believeth in him should not perish, but have ____ life" (John 3:15)
34. "The bowls, and the ____, . . . wherewith they ministered, took they away" (Jer. 52:18)
36. "To him was given the key of the bottomless ____" (Rev. 9:1)
38. "And ____ lived seventy years, and begat Abram, Nahor, and Haran" (Gen. 11:26)
42. Knock out (boxing), abbr.

43. "And Seth lived. . .and begat ____" (Gen. 5:6)
44. Average, abbr.
45. Barrels, abbr.
47. "I am the Lord that brought thee [Abram] out of ____ of the Chaldees" (Gen. 15:7)
49. "And Joshua sent men from Jericho to ____" (Josh. 7:2)
50. "____, everyone that thirsteth" (Isa. 55:1)

by Janet W. Adkins

ACROSS

1. Engrossed
5. "In God will I praise ____ word" (Ps. 56:10)
8. "The Lord came unto the prophet Gad, David's ____." (2 Sam. 24:11)
12. "Wilt thou ____ destroy the righteous with the wicked?" (Gen. 18:23)
13. "Of ____, the family of the Erites" (Num. 26:16)
14. "He would not spend the time in ____" (Acts 20:16)
15. Seriously wound
16. "But it ____ thou" (Ps. 55:13)
17. "Rejoicing, so that the city ____ again" (1 Kings 1:45)
38. Chemical suffix
20. "Let my last ____ be like his!" (Num. 23:10)
22. "There is nothing ____ for me" (1 Sam. 27:1)
25. "It is ____ a spiritual body" (1 Cor. 15:44)
29. "They are vanity, and the work of ____" (Jer. 10:15)
30. "A soft ____ turneth away wrath" (Prov. 15:1)
31. American Institute of Electronics, abbr.
32. Mine product
33. "His hands were ____ until the going down of the sun" (Exod. 17:12)
37. Girl's name
40. Exam taker
41. "It ____ fire and brimstone from heaven" (Luke 17:9)
42. Hot and cold beverage
43. "His master shall bore his ear through with an ____" (Exod. 21:6 NKJV)
44. "I will speak but this ____" (Judg. 6:39)
47. Agent, in other words, abbr.
49. Greek god of love
53. "Where the body of Jesus had ____" (John 20:12)
54. Confederate general
55. "And they ____ upon horses" (Jer. 6:23)
56. "Exceeding in ____ attire upon their heads" (Ezek. 23:15)
57. "____, of the Gentiles also" (Rom. 3:29)
58. Spit out

DOWN

1. "The ____ of consecration" (Exod. 29:27)
2. In the manner of, Fr.
3. Greek letter
4. Love apple
5. "Let them be ____ of wood" (Josh. 9:21)
6. "And ____ also the Jairite was a chief ruler about David" (2 Sam. 20:26)
7. The captain of Jabin's army (Judg. 4:7)
8. "Unto Thyatira, and unto ____" (Rev. 1:11)
9. That, Sp.
10. One, Ger.
11. Old piece of cloth
19. The father of Abner (1 Sam. 26:5)
21. Girl's name
22. "Ye shall slay the ____" (Lev. 20:15)
23. A descendant of 13-Across

24. "I see men as ____, walking" (Mark 8:24)

26. "For they had ____ with all their heart" (2 Chron. 15:15)

27. Inspiring fear

28. "____ not, nor be dismayed" (1 Chron. 22:13)

34. "____unto my cry" (Ps. 17:1)

35. River in Scotland

36. "And this man went up out of his city ____" (1 Sam. 1:3)

37. "For our vines have tender ____" (Song of Sol. 2:15)

38. "There is one ____ for them" (Lev. 7:7)

39. Tankers for refueling ships

44. "And a nourisher of thine ____ age" (Ruth 4:15)

45. "____, my son, let us not all now go" (2 Sam. 13:25)

46. Business house, Fr. abbr.

48. Shoe width

50. "And ___ up their women with child" (2 Kings 8:12)

51. Poem

52. "Woe to the women that ____ pillows to all armholes" (Ezek. 13:18)

PUZZLE 43

by Teri Grottke

ACROSS

1. The prophet who went up to heaven in a whirlwind (2 Kings 2:11)
6. A son of Jeroboam (1 Kings 14:1)
11. Moses' brother
12. Humble
13. "Even unto Ithiel and ____" (Prov. 30:1)
14. Capital of Moab (Isa. 15:1)
15. "That ___ should be a kind of firstfruits" (James 1:18)
16. Preposition
17. His Highness, abbr.
18. A snooze
21. Iron, chem. symbol
22. Giants (Deut. 9:2)
25. A minor objection
27. Europium, chem. symbol
28. "____ tempteth he any man" (James 1:13)
31. "____, supposing him to be the gardener" (John 20:15)
33. The fourth son of Midian (Gen. 25:4 NKJV)
34. "They came to _____" (2 Sam. 24:6)
35. There were 70 ____ (Exod. 1:5)
37. Smallest state, abbr.
38. Reflection of sounds
41. Not consulted
42. Ahasuerus' chamberlain (Esther 1:10)
44. Last book of the Old Testament
45. "I will praise thee with uprightness of ____" (Ps. 119:7)
49. "To the dwelling of ____" (Num. 21:15)
50. French article
51. Los Angeles, abbr.
52. General Motors, abbr.

DOWN

1. "Two years before the ____" (Amos 1:1)
2. A note to follow So
3. Eldest son of Caleb (1 Chron. 4:15)
4. Moses' mother (Exod. 6:20)
5. A son of Seir the Horite (Gen. 36:20)
6. A river of Damascus (2 Kings 5:12)
7. The general under Deborah (Judg. 4:8)
8. "Surely the Lord ____ in this place" (Gen. 28:16)
9. "There is neither ____ nor Greek" (Gal. 3:28)
10. "____, every one that thirsteth" (Isa. 55:1)
19. Pastry crust and filling
20. "David. . .dwelt in strong holds at ____" (1 Sam. 23:29)
21. "His hands shall also ____ it" (Zech. 4:9)
22. "____ the works were finished" (Heb. 4:3)
23. Nehemiah, abbr.
24. To become absorbed in thought
26. Prejudice
29. One of David's wives (1 Chron. 3:3)
30. 17th camp of Israel from Egypt (Num. 33:5–21)
32. Less soft
36. "____ I make thine enemies thy footstool" (Ps. 110:1)
39. Scorch
40. A son of Joktan (Gen. 10:28)
43. "Out of whose womb came the ____?" (Job 38:29)
44. Pa's wife
46. For example, Lat. abbr.

47. "I ____ Alpha and Omega"
    (Rev. 21:6)
48. Preposition

PUZZLE 44

by Janet Kennedy

ACROSS

1. "In the _____ God created the heaven and earth" (Gen. 1:1)
8. "And on the seventh _____ God ended his work" (Gen. 2:2)
11. "Generations of Esau, who is _____" (Gen. 36:1)
12. "The word of the _____ came unto Abram in a vision" (Gen. 15:1)
13. Prefix: again, anew, once more
14. Germanium, chem. symbol
15. "And Cain talked with _____ his brother" (Gen. 4:8)
18. Kiloliter, abbr.
19. Inches, abbr.
20. Jelly
21. Eager
23. "And I will put _____ between thee and the woman" (Gen. 3:15)
25. "Why make ye this _____, and weep? The damsel is not dead" (Mark 5:39)
27. "Cain went. . .and dwelt in the land of _____" (Gen. 4:16)
29. Address abbreviation
30. Declare
31. Surrounded by
32. Once more
34. Contraction for I am
35. "I was afraid, because I was _____; and I hid myself" (Gen. 3:10)
37. A part of a curved line
38. Not bright
40. Car manufacturer, abbr.
41. 6, Rom. num.
42. Common era, abbr.
44. Compass point, abbr.
45. "And she [Eve] bare a son. . . called. . ._____. . .another seed instead of Abel" (Gen. 4:25)

47. Not a liquid or a gas
49. Sound of a sheep
51. Hebrews, abbr.
53. The sun, Sp.
54. A young seed
56. Edge of a roof
58. Northeastern U.S., abbr.
59. "Shew you a _____ upper room furnished and prepared" (Mark 14:15)
60. Snakelike fish

DOWN

1. "In the _____ was the Word, . . . and the Word was God" (John 1:1)
2. "And the Lord God planted a garden eastward in _____; and there he put the man whom he had formed" (Gen. 2:8)
3. "_____ ye therefore, and teach all nations" (Matt. 28:19)
4. "And God said, Let us make man in our _____, after our likeness" (Gen. 1:26)
5. Not well
6. "_____ man hath seen God at any time" (John 1:18)
7. A sauce for potatoes
9. "And God said unto Noah, . . . Make thee an _____ of gopher wood" (Gen. 6:13–14)
10. "Her feathers with _____ gold" (Ps. 68:13)
16. Nickname for Benjamin
17. A tree
21. "Can a maid forget her ornaments, or a bride her _____?" (Jer. 2:32)
22. "Obed: he is the father of Jesse, the father of _____" (Ruth 4:17)

24. "And Abraham called. . .his son . . .whom Sarah bare to him, ____" (Gen. 21:3)
26. Kingdom
28. One of Shobal's children (Gen. 36:23)
32. Confused, nervous
33. Virginia's neighbor, abbr.
36. "And Adam called his wife's name ____" (Gen. 3:20)
39. A group of songs combined to make one song
43. "____, everyone that thirsteth" (Isa. 55:1)
45. "Then ____, (who also is called Paul,)" (Acts 13:9)

46. "____ leadeth me beside the still waters" (Ps. 23:2)
47. "One lawgiver, who is able to ____ and to destroy" (James 4:12)
48. Library Science, abbr.
49. "And God said, . . .I do set my ____ in the cloud, . . .a token of a covenant" (Gen. 9:12–13)
50. Avenue, abbr.
52. A honey maker
54. Fa, so, ____, ti
56. Electrical Engineer, abbr.

PUZZLE 45

by Janet W. Adkins

ACROSS

1. Croaker
5. "The priest shall pronounce him clean: it is but a ____" (Lev. 13:6)
9. Female sibling, for short
12. South American country
13. Layer
14. Gold, Sp.
15. "And they bowed their heads, and made ____" (Gen. 43:28)
17. Familiar name for Saul's son (1 Sam. 14:42)
18. "Master, the Jews of ____ sought to stone thee" (John 11:8)
19. "Then Saul fell straightway all ____ on the earth" (1 Sam. 28:20)
20. "Though thou shouldest bray a fool in a mortar among wheat with a ____" (Prov. 27:22)
23. Plural suffix
24. "And be ye kind ____ to another" (Eph. 4:32)
25. "Stolen ____ are sweet" (Prov. 9:17)
28. "Woe unto them that draw iniquity. . .and sin as it were with a cart ____" (Isa. 5:18)
30. "The liberal soul shall be made ____" (Prov. 11:25)
31. Conceited person
33. "Cut the bars of iron in ____" (Ps. 107:16)
35. Before, poetic
36. Talking horse
37. "And the harp, and the viol, and the ____. . ." (Isa. 5:12)
40. "They fell on their ____: and they said, The Lord he is the God" (1 Kings 18:39)
42. Volcano output
43. Burned residue

44. "If. . .I may provoke to ____ them which are my flesh" (Rom. 11:14)
49. Black sticky substance
50. "And his allowance was a. . .daily ____ for every day" (2 Kings 25:30)
51. Sharpen
52. Compass point, abbr.
53. "Thou sawest the feet and ____" (Dan. 2:41)
54. Precipitation

DOWN

1. Fleet post office, abbr.
2. Confederate soldier
3. Mine product
4. "But thou shalt put away the ____ of innocent blood from Israel" (Deut. 19:13)
5. "For I have learned, in whatsoever ____ I am, therewith to be content" (Phil. 4:11)
6. Motion picture
7. Atomic Energy Commission, abbr.
8. "That the ____ may be waved for a wave offering" (Lev. 7:30)
9. "For I am a stranger with thee, and a ____ as all my fathers were" (Ps. 39:12)
10. "Thou shalt not lift up any ____ tool upon them" (Deut. 27:5)
11. "And he hath put a new ____ in my mouth" (Ps. 40:3)
16. My Gal ____
20. For, Sp.
21. "And Seth. . .begat ____" (Gen. 5:6)
22. "Their throat is an open ____" (Ps. 5:9)
23. "And they shall ____ the flesh in that night, roast with fire" (Exod. 12:8)

25. "Joshua made _____ a long time with all those kings" (Josh. 11:18)
26. Einstienium, chem. symbol
27. Painful
29. Printer's measure
30. "When saw we thee an hungered and _____ thee?" (Matt. 25:37)
32. Wager
34. "The _____ shall rejoice and blossom as the rose" (Isa. 35:1)
37. "And their words seemed to them as idle _____" (Luke 24:11)
38. "The king of Assyria brought men from Babylon. . .Cuthah, and from _____" (2 Kings 17:24)

39. Twenty thousand measures of barley, and twenty thousand _____ of wine" (2 Chron. 2:10)
40. Destiny
41. Belonging to Abia's son (Matt. 1:7)
42. Ancient musical instrument
45. Late Chinese Communist Chairman
46. Charged particle
47. "The children of Lod, Hadid, and _____" (Ezra 2:33)
48. Not old

PUZZLE 46

by Janet Kennedy

ACROSS

1. Disney deer
6. Giver
11. Belonging to Robert E.
12. Girl's name
14. "I am like an ____ of the desert" (Ps. 102:6)
16. Wipe clean
18. Adam's companion
20. Peach state, abbr.
21. The main central parts of churches
22. Impersonal pronoun
23. *Exodus* author, Leon ____
26. Price mark-down
28. Esau's pottage was made from this legume (Gen. 25:34)
30. Cain did this to the ground (Gen. 4:2)
32. Digital audiotape, abbr.
33. Tree trunk
34. Horned African mammals
37. "Yea, the sparrow hath found an house. . .even thine ____, O Lord of hosts" (Ps. 84:3)
40. "Thou anointest my ____ with oil" (Ps. 23:5)
41. "It shall bruise thy head, and thou shalt bruise his ____" (Gen. 3:15)
42. You, KJV English
43. Stay away from
46. Nickel, chem. symbol
47. Physicians, abbr.
49. Naaman was one of these because of his disease (2 Kings 5:1)
50. "My tongue is the ____ of a ready writer" (Ps. 45:1)
51. Social equal

53. "The wringing of the ____ bringeth forth blood" (Prov. 30:33)
55. "A time to mourn, and a time to ____" (Eccles. 3:4)
56. Game

DOWN

2. "Israel loved Joseph more than ____" (Gen. 37:3)
3. Myself
4. Existed
5. God's chosen nation
6. To abandon
7. Metals
8. A silver-white metal, abbr.
9. "Ye are all ____ in Christ" (Gal. 3:28)
10. A bump in a ski slope
13. Doled
15. "A certain man, which had devils long time, and ____ no clothes" (Luke 8:27)
17. Address abbreviation
19. Foul
24. Asian nation
25. "____ fast therefore in liberty" (Gal. 5:1)
26. Slow-moving mammal
27. Seaweed
29. International Trade Organization, abbr.
31. Sick
34. Poem
35. Pay attention to
36. Harsh
37. Strangers
38. French name
39. What David used to kill Goliath
43. Man's name
44. Kind of modern art

45. Fall
48. Health facility
50. Apiece
52. Printer's measure
54. Therefore

by Teri Grottke

ACROSS

1. Tiny insect
4. Facts
9. Undergraduate degree, abbr.
11. "By his name ____" (Ps. 68:4)
12. "____, and make thy bed" (Acts 9:34)
13. Small arms ammunition, abbr.
14. "____ Lord God! behold" (Jer. 1:6)
15. Liquid extracted from a fruit
16. "In the province of ____" (Dan. 8:2)
17. A family of returning Nethinims (Neh. 7:48)
19. Scold
21. 1004, Rom. num.
22. Walked at the head of the line
23. Bedad's son (Gen. 36:35)
24. Give instruction
27. Single
28. Decay
30. Exclamation
31. Brawling
34. Capture
37. Not, prefix
38. Traps (Ps. 140:5)
39. Preposition
40. "Ye shall be. . .____ upon her knees" (Isa. 66:12)
43. Announced
47. Heber's father (Luke 3:35)
48. "And ____ also the Jairite" (2 Sam. 20:26)
49. "They must ____ be borne" (Jer. 10:5)
51. Neither
52. Male adults
53. Jehaleleel's son (1 Chron. 4:16)
54. Expire

DOWN

1. Zibeon's son (Gen. 36:24)
2. "Azariah, Raamiah, ____ " (Neh. 7:7)
3. Thorium, chem. symbol
4. Smear
5. Opera solos
6. Muscle twitch
7. One who takes advantage
8. Myself
9. Chief idol of the Canaanites
10. Identical
13. Slip
15. Indonesian island
16. Always
18. This man had 70 sons (Judg. 8:30)
20. Father of Hophni (1 Sam. 1:3)
23. Aaron's grave (Num. 20:27–28)
24. Daylight time, abbr.
25. Son of Caleb (1 Chron. 4:8)
26. Definite article
28. Hospital caregiver, abbr.
29. King of Bashan (Num. 21:33)
32. Implement
33. Baby
34. Iniquity
35. Terminates
36. Land surrounded by water
38. One of the twelve spies (Num. 13:11)
40. "And the fallow ____ " (Deut. 14:5)
41. One of Christ's words on the cross (Mark 15:34)
42. Challenge
43. Unclear
44. Before
45. Able
46. Real estate investment, abbr.
50. Southern continent, abbr.

by Janet Kennedy

ACROSS

1. "And the ferret, and the ____, and the lizard" (Lev. 11:30)
6. "A living ____ is better than a dead lion" (Eccles. 9:4)
9. "The ____ of money that Haman had promised" (Esther 4:7)
10. "As a ____ robbed of her whelps in the field" (2 Sam. 17:8)
11. Put into a capsule form
15. Man's name
16 "Judas. . .drew near unto Jesus to ____ him" (Luke 22:47)
17. "And the river shall bring forth ____ abundantly" (Exod. 8:3)
18. Elevated railroad
20. "They all are brass, and ____, and iron" (Ezek. 22:18)
21. Married woman's title
23. "And God created great ____," (Gen. 1:21)
28. Exclamation of doubt or surprise
29. Card that tells who you are, abbr.
30. "Five loaves and the two ____" (Mark 6:41)
33. Field officer, abbr.
34. Compound, abbr.
35. An explosive material
36. "The swine. . .ran violently down a ____ place into the sea" (Mark 5:13)
38. "I am like a ____ of the wilderness" (Ps. 102:6)
41. "David took an ____ and played with his hand" (1 Sam. 16:23)
42. Gloomy; ill-humored
43. Egg, prefix
45. "The Lord had laid on him the iniquity of ____ all" (Isa. 53:6)
46. Massachusetts neighbor, abbr.

48. "There came a ____ out of the heat, and fastened on his hand" (Acts 28:3)
52. Dover's state, abbr.
53. A thought
55. "I have given ____ unto the children of Lot" (Deut. 2:9)
56. "And the ____ shalt thou trample under feet" (Ps. 91:13)
57. "And the ____, and the pelican" (Lev. 11:18)

DOWN

1. "The night hawk, and the ____, and the hawk" (Lev. 11:16)
2. "The cruel venom of ____" (Deut. 32:33)
3. A salt-water mollusk
4. A large Australian bird
5. "Or wings and feathers unto the ____?" (Job 39:13)
6. Belief God has no influence on man
7. "And all that handle the ____, the mariners" (Ezek. 27:29)
8. "And the ____ shall be a burden" (Eccles. 12:5)
12. "Joshua sent men from Jericho to ____" (Josh. 7:2)
13. At the back of the boat
14. A long period of time
19. A liberal or radical
22. To direct the attention
24. Large African mammals, for short
25. "And stingeth like an ____" (Prov. 23:32)
26. "Have ye received the Holy Ghost ____ ye believed?" (Acts 19:2)
27. Esther, abbr.

31. Station, abbr.
32. Einsteinium, chem. symbol
37. Each, abbr.
39. One who loves
40. "For there is ____ respect of persons with God" (Rom. 2:11)
42. "They have caused him to ride upon the king's ____" (1 Kings 1:44)
44. Eggs
47. "Why make ye this ____, and weep?" (Mark 5:39)
49. Dog's foot
50. Historical period

51. Doctor of divinity, abbr.
52. Inspector general, abbr.
53. To cause to be, prefix

PUZZLE 49

by Janet W. Adkins

ACROSS

1. "And her ____ was to light on a part of the field belonging unto Boaz" (Ruth 2:3)
4. "And ____ gave names to all cattle" (Gen. 2:20)
8. Not fast
12. See 17-Across "____ ye come out. . ."
13. "Master, the Jews of ____ sought to stone thee" (John 11:8)
14. Ankle bones
15. "How are the ____ fallen" (2 Sam. 1:27)
17. "Are ye come out. . .with swords and with ____ to take me?" (Mark 14:48)
19. "Take thine ____, eat, drink, and be merry" (Luke 12:19)
21. Expunge
22. "Woe is me, . . .that I dwell in the tents of ____!" (Ps. 120:5)
25. "Made the fourteenth day of the month ____ a day of gladness" (Esther 9:19)
27. Ogle
28. "The children of Shallum, . . .of ____, of Talmon" (Ezra 2:42)
29. Spanish Mrs., abbr.
32. "The governor under ____ the king kept the city of the Damascenes with a garrison" (2 Cor. 11:32)
34. "And ____ was as light of foot as a wild roe" (2 Sam. 2:18)
36. Falstaff's follower
37. "Honour the face of the old man, and ____ thy God" (Lev. 19:32)
39. "Then Job arose, and ____ his mantle" (Job 1:20)
40. "It had been good for that man if he had not been ____" (Matt. 26:24)
41. Trig functions
42. "____ into his gates with thanksgiving" (Ps. 100:4)

45. Chop finely
47. Scold
49. "The carved images, and the ____ images" (2 Chron. 34:3)
53. You are, Sp.
54. Mend a sock
56. Anger
57. "There was a continual ____ given him of the king of Babylon" (Jer. 52:34)
58. Ballet position
59. Each

DOWN

1. "And Noah begat Shem, ____, and Japheth" (Gen. 5:32)
2. Onassis
3. Cribbage pin
4. "Zacharias which perished between the ____ and the temple" (Luke 11:51)
5. "In those ____ also saw I Jews that had married wives of Ashdod" (Neh. 13:23)
6. Preposition
7. French pronoun
8. Brenda or Belle
9. Volcano output
10. Spanish cheers
11. "Hear instruction and be ____" (Prov. 8:33)
16. "I will praise the Lord with my whole ____" (Ps. 111:1)
18. "Mine eye poureth out ____ unto God" (Job 16:20)
20. "Therefore shall they ____ of the fruit of their own way" (Prov. 1:31)
22. Part of KKK
23. Weird, alt. spelling
24. Believe
26. "Hath translated us into the kingdom of his ____ Son" (Col. 1:13)
28. Tribe of Anna the prophetess (Luke 2:36)

29. "Then Samuel took a stone, and set it between Mizpeh and ____" (1 Sam. 7:12)
30. French name
31. Heights, in other words, abbr.
33. "Lay siege against it, and built a ____ ____ against it" (Ezek. 4:2) (2 words)
35. "Woe to ____. . .the city where David dwelt!" (Isa. 29:1)
38. Conjunction
40. "But let man and ____ be covered with sackcloth" (Jon. 3:8)
41. Scottish quick bread
42. "And Gaal the son of ____ came with his brethren" (Judg. 9:26)

43. In Luke's geneology of Christ, the father of Salathiel (Luke 3:27)
44. "Shall these. . .natural branches, be grated into their own olive ____?" (Rom. 11:24)
46. Father of Zaccur (Neh. 3:2)
48. Electronic data processing, abbr.
50. "That he may dip the ____ of his finger in water" (Luke 16:24)
51. "Sir, come down ____ my child die" (John 4:49)
52. "The captain of his host was Abner, the son of ____, Saul's uncle" (1 Sam. 14:50)
55. Alvin, Albert, or Allen

PUZZLE 50

ACROSS

1. "Keep me as the ____ of the eye" (Ps. 17:8)
5. A person who runs errands
11. "For the ____ which is lent to the Lord" (1 Sam. 2:20)
12. A citrus fruit the color of its name
13. Second day of the week, abbr.
14. "And the ____ father shall say unto the elders" (Deut. 22:16)
16. "Wert graffed contrary to nature into a good ____ tree" (Rom 11:24)
17. Fa, so, ____, ti
18. A shot for an air rifle
19. "When thou was under the ____ tree, I saw thee" (John 1:48)
20. "Orpah kissed her mother in law, but ____ clave unto her" (Ruth 1:14)
22. District Attorney, abbr.
24. "Our Lord, and his Christ; and he shall ____ for ever and ever" (Rev. 11:15)
26. Common Era, abbr.
27. "I ____ that bread of life" (John 6:48)
28. "The sons of Ram . . . were, Maaz, and Jamin, and ____" (1 Chron. 2:27)
30. "And Jacob took him rods of the . . . hazel and ____ tree" (Gen. 30:37)
34. "Where neither moth ____ rust doth corrupt" (Matt. 6:20)
35. Advertisement, abbr.
36. Old Testament, abbr.
37. "There is none that doeth good, no, not ____" (Ps. 14:3)
38. To be idle
39. Spills water upon
41. California city, for short
42. Heat, abbr.
45. "When thou shalt hear a sound going in the tops of the ____ trees . . . thou shalt go out to battle" (1 Chron. 14:15)
50. Book that follows Jeremiah, abbr.
51. A vein of metal ore
52. A sour fruit used to make a cool drink

DOWN

1. "I see a rod of an ____ tree" (Jer. 1:11)
2. "Go, wash in the ____ of Siloam" (John 9:7)
3. A great fear causing loss of control
4. Lane, abbr.
5. "The ____ tree, . . . even all the trees of the field, are withered" (Joel 1:12)
6. American Rocket Society, abbr.
7. A Scottish Highlander
8. "For I will cast out the nations before thee, and ____ thy borders" (Exod. 34:24)
9. Brigadier generals, abbr.
10. Old English, abbr.
14. Rebels
15. "Thou that ____ idols, dost thou commit sacrilege?" (Rom. 2:22)
18. Bachelor of Theology, abbr.
21. "I found an alter with this inscription, TO THE ____ GOD" (Acts 27:23)
23. Air Coordinating Committee, abbr.
25. A large Australian bird
26. To give up
29. A very long time
31. "And Jacob took him rods . . . of the ____ and chestnut tree" (Gen. 30:37)

32. "But the answer of a good conscience _____ God" (1 Peter 3:21)
33. An examination of knowledge
38. A green citrus fruit
40. "_____ word is a lamp unto my feet" (Ps. 119:105)
41. A northern constellation
44. Unidentified flying object, abbr.
46. "There was a man in the land of _____, whose name was Job" (Job 1:1)
47. Bachelor of law, abbr.
48. Again, anew, once more, suffix
49. "But that the world through him might _____ saved" (John 3:17)

ANSWERS

Puzzle 1

```
L A Z A R U S   W I N E
O   E N   T A L E N T     L
S A N D     M I D     P R E
T   A S   P A N D A     E A
S O N   V I R G I N S     V
H I   M I N I O N     O E
E L M   N E T   G     W O N
E   A   E D A M   N E W
P E N N Y   N   T A R E S S
    T A     S H O T     S H
M E T   R A   A W E D     A
  C A N D L E   E I L L
R O C K   P R O D I G A L
```

Puzzle 2

```
N E W   A C T S   O R B S
O     A D O   O R D A I N
I R V   A T   E D G E
S E   E A C H   A     R N
E V E N   H E L P E R   E
  E   E G O   E V E   W
A N G E L   C A R E F U L
B T U   D I A L   R   N Y
L I N E   M A N Y   D
E D   S K I P   A   S O N
  E A S E   H O S T   N A
A   S   P R O   T O T E M
P S A L T E R   Y E N   E
```

Puzzle 3

```
N O W   E G G S   P R A Y
A D A   P E L E   H A L O
N O R   N A E   A M E N
A R M A G E D D O N
  H A S   S I U   S E
L O T   D I D   L E A P T
O B O E   S I T   L I O N
S A T A N   E R A   M T A
E L   S O L   A S S
    T H E O P H I L U S
N O N E   A B P   A R E
E W E R   D E E D   M I A
T E E N   A D D S   P M S
```

Puzzle 4

```
T H E   E S T H E R
  A   W V   O A R   S   J
  G O   E   O N   S H U A
M A R A   N   N   H E R E
I R A D   A A T E     L
R   J O C H E B E D
I   M O   M E   A G E D
A B I G A I L   F   L O
M   C L   L O O   A
  S H A L L   R A H A B
A S A   E A T   I D
D E L I L A H   T A M A R
O   N A H A M   H H I
```

104

Puzzle 5

Puzzle 6

Puzzle 7

Puzzle 8

Puzzle 9

Puzzle 10

Puzzle 11

Puzzle 12

Puzzle 13

Puzzle 14

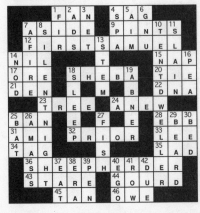

Puzzle 15

Puzzle 16

Puzzle 17

Puzzle 18

Puzzle 19

Puzzle 20

Puzzle 21

Puzzle 22

Puzzle 23

```
 1 J  2 O  3 S  4 H  5 U  A     6 I     B  L  7 E  A  8 M
11 U  R  I     12 S  T  O  N  E     14 A  R  A
15 D  E  C  16 K     17 S  H  E     18 B  R  E  D
    G     19 K  E  20 E  P     21 A  L  A  S     22 E
23 E  24 D  25 P  L  A  N  T  26 E  D     27 A  S
28 S  O  29 N  T  A  K  E     30 B  E  A  31 S  T
   32 T  O  33 M  E  34 B  A     35 G  I
36 B  E  R  E  37 A     38 M  I  N  D  E  D  39 I  40
41 E  D  42 A  N  Y  43    44 T  O  E  45 E  R
    A  46 A  S  D  O     47 E  N  A  M  48 P
49 S  I  N  E  50 U     51 T     52 F  I  R  E
53 T  I  E     54 M  I  G  H  T  55    56 L  I  E
57 S  T  R  E  E  T     58 A  B  D  E  E  L
```

Puzzle 24

```
 1 A  2 B  3 I  4 G  5 A  6 I  L     7 L  A  8 M  P  9 S
    E     10 U  M  M  A  H  11    O     E
12 F  E  13 A  R     14 A  M  E  N  15    16 O  W  E
17 E  L  I     18 G  E  N  U  I  N  E
19 E  Z  20 R  A     E     M     21 P  S
    E     22 D  23 R  S  24    25 B  E  A  26 T
27 O  B  E  D  I  E  N  C  E     B     28 L
    U     B     A     29 R  E  I     E
30 A  B  Y  S  S     K     32 R  E  V
   N     O     33 34 35 E  A  R  A  I
   G  36 K  I  N  G  37 38 H  E  L  M
39 E  Y  E     E     40 A  A     41 O  X
   L  42 S  T  U  M  B  L  I  N  G
```

Puzzle 25

```
 1 B  2 R  3 I  C  4 K  M  A  K  5 I  N  6 G     7 B
   R  8 T  O     9 A  T     10 11 R  E  A
12 A  S  13 N  14 E  15 E  16 D  L  E  W  O  R  K
   Z     17 F  U  L  L  E  R     S     E
18 I  19 G     E     A     20 21 S  I  R
22 E  A  23 C  A  24 R  25 P  26 E  N  T  E  R  S
28 R  R  T     29 P  O  T  T  E  R  S
30 S  D  31 32 I  N  S  T  E     O
   34 35 E  D  O  M  36 37 T  A  N  N  E  R  S  38
39 A  N  O  N  40 R  E  D     41 A  A
42 C  E  43 44 E  M  B  R  O  45 46 47 I  D  E  R  Y
48 R  A  R  E     50 L  A  K  E
51 S  T  S  52 C  A  U  L  K  E  R  S
```

Puzzle 26

```
 1 I  2 S  3 R  4 A  E  L     5 S  6 R     7 S  8 E
 9 M  L     10 R  11 12 I  G  H  T  E  O  U  S
13 P  U  A  H     16 B  R  I  E  F     17 E  A
18 O  M  R  I     19 N  E  20 W  I     U
21 S  B  22 23 G  R  I  E  V  A  N  C  E  25
26 S  E  C  H  U     28 T  A  R  E  A  29 I
30 I  R  P  E  E  L  31 D     32 33 L  A  D
   B     S     34 O  U  R  35 36 A  N  D
37 L  O  38 39 F  T  Y  40 41 42 E  S  T  E  E  M  43
44 E  V  E     45 46 E  G  Y  P  T  47 H  E  R
48 E  A  R     R     E     50 F     51 R  I
52 I  R  R  E  F  U  T  A  B  L  E
   F  57 D  E  B  A  T  E     58 W  O  N
```

Puzzle 27

```
 1 P  2 E  3 A  4 R  5 L  S     6 J  7 A  8 S  9 P  10 E  11 R
12 E  X  I  S  T     13 C  14 T  H  E  S  E
15 D  O  D     16 R  H  O     18 A  K  C
19 A  D  S     20 H  E  R  B  S  21    22 L  I  E
23 N  U     24 G  R  A  Y  I  S  H  25    26 M  D
27 T  S  A  R     S     29 30 O  B  O  E
   31 D  E  A  C  O  N  E  S  S
32 33 B  L  O  B     P     34 35 36 E  A  C  H
37 E  A  38 39 40 E  M  E  R  A  L  D  41 42 43 O  E
44 R  N  A  45 46 O  P  A  L  S     47 A  Y  E
48 Y  D  S     49 A  S  A     50 G  O  D
51 L  A  S  S  52 53 O  E  54 55 A  G  A  T  E
56 S  U  R  E  T  Y     57 S  N  A  R  E  D
```

Puzzle 28

```
              1 E  2 A  3 S  4 T
           5 R  E  P  A  I  R  6
        7 M  A  R     8 I  M  N  A  9
       10 C  A  N     11 S  N  E  A  K  S  12
    13 L  A  R     14 N  E  T  S     15 H  E  A  16
    17 A  N  A  N  I  A  S     19 L  A  M  B  20 S
    21 M  D     22 A  N  T     23 S  A  I  24 R  O
    25 P  L  A  T  E     27 S  E  N  A  T  O  R  28
       29 E  R  I     30 S  P  E  D     31 E  A  T
       32 33 M  O  R  T  A  R     34 B  A  D
          35 N  E  A  R     36 A  A  R
          37 B  R  E  A  C  H  38
          39 E  D  I  T
```

108

Puzzle 29

```
R U N   A C R E   A M O N
I T   C P A   O S P R A Y
V   M A   L A   H O S T
E D   S E E R   U   H E
R E N T   B R I N G S   L
  P   L A   E R I   D
P A V E D   S A M A R I A
A R E   O N E S   S   N D
I T S   R A M S   V
N E   R E A P   I   S A T
  D E A D   G R   D O
A   O   G I N   H E B E R
C O N T E N T   T I E   N
```

Puzzle 30

```
C R I M S O N   B R A S S
O E   E O N   B L U E   C
P B   U C   A A R   L A
P U R P L E   A C A D   R
E K E   O   K L   E L
R E D D I S H   A T E
  T   A L I   G O L D   T
B H   Y E L L O W   V I
R   V   L E V I   B
A   G L U E D   A S E R
S I R   G R E E N   O S O
E T A   L   A N Y   R A W
N A Y   Y E T   S U N
```

Puzzle 31

```
B E D   S A W N   C A R E
  R A I N Y   T O   U L
A I   B E T   F E M A L E
S D   E V E N   N E G E V
P L A T E   A P   T O R E
H E M   M I R T H   S N
E   S H I N A R   S   T
M I D I A N   Y A H W E H
E   O T   S E E P   L
  G U I T A R   M A D
V E S P E R S   L A V E R
O R   S   E E   C R E S T
W A Y   A L L   D A R T
```

Puzzle 32

```
E V E   P U A   A H A B
B E S T   I N N   S A L E
E R L E   E N A   E R S E
R A I L   C I N N A M O N
  A B E   I E
S H A V E   C A R E F U L
L E V I   W A S   N O T E
T R A V A I L   A T R E E
  R N   A I R
E L E M E N T S   E A R S
V I L E   E R S   A L I E
I M L A   T I E   T I D E
L E S T   H M S   A E R
```

Puzzle 33

```
L A B A N S   K C
A D O N I R A M   E O S
S O   I N   H A M   R M C
S U M M E R   R A B B A H
  B E   A I   T I E
A L L   O N   L E A H S
S E E   E T A M   H O T
A D A M S   Y E   I R
  E R E   E D   A S
H I N N O M   T O P H E T
E B B   M I L   O O   M R
L O A   N A C R E   E I
P S   S P A S M   N G
```

Puzzle 34

```
S O M E T I M E S   U A W
E R A S U R E   H O S E A
E E   T N   T H E R E   I
K   S E E K   U   D   T
I V E   S O U G H T   W I
N E E D   A N   D I V A N
G E K   B K   M   I G
  E M   S E E K E S T
U N T I M E L Y   P E D
N   H G   A I   W A I T
I T   H I R E D   R H G
T E N T   C F   E L I   O
E A S Y   H   W A I T E D
```

109

Puzzle 35

```
HID    PEEP   HOMO
ADO    EVES   AMOS
MERARI    SCHEME
    HILT   RAISE
BASIL    USES
AGAR   PITA    ACT
BEWARE   AMASAI
YES   ARMY   REND
    AGES   ARRAY
AFORE   HALO
DIVIDE    TOWERS
AVES   BEEN   RIG
MERE   BARE   NET
```

Puzzle 36

Puzzle 37

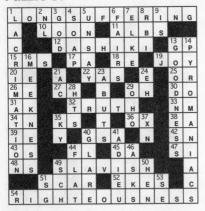

Puzzle 38

Puzzle 39

Puzzle 40

Puzzle 41

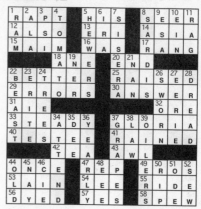

```
F R Y I N G P A N   A R C
L     M O O   D I S H     R
A W E     B O     H   A U
G A   C A L F   B O W L S
O T   U S E T H   W   E E
N E   P A T       P R
  R O S S   N   P L A T E
S P D     R E P L A N   T
P O E T S   V I A     M E
O T   E   K E T T L E   E
O   A R B O R   T   N U N
N A V A L     H E   O R A
S I G H S   F O R K S   L
```

Puzzle 42

```
R A P T   H I S   S E E R
A L S O   E R I   A S I A
M A I M   W A S   R A N G
      A N E   E N D
B E T T E R   R A I S E D
E R R O R S   A N S W E R
A I E           O R E
S T E A D Y   G L O R I A
T E S T E E   R A I N E D
      T E A   A W L
O N C E   R E P   E R O S
L A I N   L E E   R I D E
D Y E D   Y E S   S P E W
```

Puzzle 43

```
E L I J A H   A B I J A H   O
A A R O N   A B A S E     O
R   U C A L   A R   W E
T O   H H   N A P       E
H   F E   A N A K I M   N
Q U I B B L E       E U   G
U   N E I T H E R   S H E
A B I D A H   G I L E A D
K   S   S O U L S     R I
E C H O   U N A S K E D
  H   B I G T H A     E
M A L A C H I   H E A R T
A R   L E   L A   G M   O
```

Puzzle 44

```
B E G I N N I N G   D A Y
E D O M   L O R D   R E
G E   A B E L   A     K L
I N   G E L   A V I D   L
N   E N M I T Y   A D O
N O D     S T   A V O W
I N   A G A I N   I M
N A K E D   A R C   D I M
G M   V I   C E H   H   N E
    S E T H   S O L I D
B A A   H E B   A   S O L
O V U L E   E A V E   N E
W   L A R G E     E E L   Y
```

Puzzle 45

```
F R O G   S C A B   S I S
P E R U   T I E R   O R O
O B E I S A N C E   J O N
    L A T E   A L O N G
P E S T L E   E S U
O N E   W A T E R S
R O P E   F A T   S N O B
  S U N D E R     E R E
    L E D   T A B R E T
F A C E S   L A V A
A S H   E M U L A T I O N
T A R   R A T E   H O N E
E S E   T O E S   S N O W
```

Puzzle 46

```
  B A M B I   D O N O R
M   L E E S   E R I N   M
O W L   E R A S E   E V E
G A   N A V E S   I T
U R I S   E R   S A L E
L E N T I L   T I L L E D
  D A T     L O G
R H I N O S   A L T A R S
H E A D   E L   H E E L
Y E   A V O I D   N I
M D S   L E P E R   P E N
E   P E E R   N O S E   G
  D A N C E   S P O R T
```

Puzzle 47

Puzzle 48

Puzzle 49

Puzzle 50